THE TRUTH ABOUT THE LIES

WORKBOOK AND JOURNAL
TO GUIDE YOU TO
YOUR TRUTH

Sharon Matthews Fortune

(Edited by Lisa Y. Burrus)

SMF media

Library of Congress Cataloging-in-Publication Data
Matthews Fortune, Sharon
    The truth about the lies: workbook and journal to guide you to your truth/Sharon Matthews Fortune

Printed in the United States of America

First Printing, 2021

ISBN 978-1-7361737-1-8 (paperback)

Publishers Disclaimer:
This publication is not intended to be used as a substitute for psychotherapy or treatment from your personal mental health professional. Readers are advised to consult their own qualified health professional regarding the treatment of mental health or medical conditions as this book does not dispense professional advice. This book contains fictional components. Characters and events are either the product of the author's imagination, perception, or interpretation. The information is not intended to diagnose, treat, cure or prevent any mental health or emotional disturbance. In the event you use any of the information in this book for personal circumstances, the author and the publisher assume no responsibility for your actions.

CONTENTS

ACKNOWLEDGEMENTS

I wish to express my gratitude to the many women and men who supported my first book, *The Truth About The Lies, What Women Tell Themselves That Keep Them Stuck With Cheating Men*. Your continuous encouragement and positive feedback motivated me to continue on my journey as an author. I pray the message in my books blesses each reader immeasurably.

I am appreciative to Lisa Y. Burrus, for editorial excellence, and Edward Broaddus, for technical expertise. I cannot thank you both enough for continuing to share your time, talents, and wisdom. Your contributions to this workbook, and to *The Truth About The Lies* brand, have been a precious gift. Last, but not least, my deepest appreciation goes to my amazing daughter Cameron, for being there for me day-to-day in more ways than I can mention. Words cannot express the depth of my love for you.

INTRODUCTION

Ladies, this is an invitation for you to do your work! By now you have read *The Truth About The Lies What Women Tell Themselves That Keep Them Stuck With Cheating Men,* the self-help guide which explores what happens when you stay in relationships with cheating men unaware of the lies you are telling yourself that keep you stuck. It shows how the lies lead to abandoning yourself and descending into a character image of a woman you never intended to become. It speaks to you from the view of the character images showing how distinctively different women from all walks of life, although never laying eyes on or speaking to one another, share a common pattern of thinking in order to avoid the pain and devastation of the reality of being with a cheater.

This workbook and journal begins where the self-help guide ended. Because of the separation from self, *The Truth About The Lies* self-help guide is written to make you aware of the character image that has hijacked your life. The companion workbook and journal speak directly to you. It is a tool to spark a reconnection with your truth; your core values, your true beliefs, and your primary needs. It challenges The Blind, The Manipulator, The Finger-Pointer, The Dreamer, The Helpless, The Settler, The Savior, and The Compromiser to boldly cut through the lies casting down every misbelief that blocks the truth.

Gaining insight to reveal your truth is not found in having immediate answers, you find it in asking yourself the right series of questions. The conclusions you jumped to in the past because of emotional wounds intensified your emotional turmoil. This workbook and journal seek to help you formulate the right questions to eliminate the rationalizations and generalizations that feed the lies you tell yourself. The best questions are created by and develop through your experiences with your cheating man. The questions you ask of yourself are valuable, more valuable than the answers that you create while you are still hurting and vulnerable. Asking the right questions will lead you to the truth about the lies and get you unstuck.

I intend for the questions asked in this workbook and journal to lead you back down the path to your core values, beliefs, and needs. Sometimes it's easier to draw a straight line when we go

1

back to where things got off track and then journey forward. The blurred boundary lines will become clear, the roadblocks will be removed, and the crossroads won't lead you down the wrong path when you ask yourself the right questions. The questions are unique to the lies each character in *The Truth About The Lies* self-help guide tells herself. They speak to the core of your true self in order to cast off the need for the characterization. As you begin your journey, I ask that you be bold, be brave, but most of all be willing to embrace the truth.

PART 1

"THE BLIND"

"The Blind," as defined in The Truth About The Lies self-help guide, cannot see what is right in front of her. She will stumble into and trip over evidence that her man is cheating, but she cannot see what is there. What "The Blind" learns to do when continuously exposed to facts that clearly suggest her man is cheating is dull her senses so she can successfully maneuver around the obvious without seeing. If this way of coping fits you best, then you will have to take the blinders off to reveal your truth.

Maneuvering around the obvious requires you to rationalize, generalize, and minimize facts, and this is always necessary when you try to avoid, deny, or resist the truth. As "The Blind," in order to challenge the lies you tell yourself, you have to enhance your sense of self-observation. When you observe yourself moving into the analytical mode that breeds the maze of irrelevant distractions, revert to the facts for your truth. Redirect yourself to view the simple, straight-forward facts that are obviously being avoided. All you need will be there and will assist with you asking yourself the right questions to reveal your truth.

1 IF ONLY I HAD PROOF

When you morphed into "The Blind" you professed the need for proof your man is cheating. However, when tripping over and running into clear signs of his cheating, you act as if you don't see the obvious. You have become a master at minimizing and rationalizing his behavior because you don't want to accept the obvious. His alibis are as weak as water and flimsy as paper, but you choose to analyze the facts and get lost in the haze of irrelevant self-imposed questions to avoid the truth that he is cheating. The lie, "If Only I Had Proof" is dangerous because choosing to be blind will make you doubt your better judgment.

As long as you are "The Blind," your man will continue to cheat. He is essentially safe to continue to be the cheater he is because the truth is, you don't really want the proof of his cheating. What you want is to be in a relationship with a faithful man. Getting proof will threaten your future, because as long as you choose not to see, you get to stay in the relationship with him without feeling foolish, stupid, or used. This could continue forever, and the longer it does, the emptier and more broken you become. As long as you are "The Blind" you won't be alone, you will always have your cheating man.

To reveal your truth, ask yourself:

1. What facts am I altering, rewriting, and excluding? What part of the situation or circumstances am I rephrasing to suit what I want to believe?

   _____

   _____

   _____

2. What do I want to believe? Does this truly reflect the facts as they exist? Given the facts, is what I want to believe possible?

   _____

_____

_____

3. What does my better judgment and logic reveal about the current situation? Am I willing to trust my judgment and logical reasoning?

_____

_____

_____

4. What am I trying to avoid by becoming blind? What does not feel right, what needs are not being met, and what evidence am I neglecting to acknowledge? Are the facts of my man's behavior inconsistent with what I choose to believe?

_____

_____

_____

5. What are the actions of a faithful man? Is this consistent with how my man acts?

_____

_____

_____

6. What boundaries have I set in this relationship? Which of my own boundaries have I violated? What led me to violate my boundaries?

_____

_____

_____

7. In reality, have I chosen to stay with a cheater? Do I regret my choice to stay with a cheater? What have I lost because of this choice, and will staying help me regain what is lost?

_____

_____

_____

8. Am I proud to be in this relationship? Does this relationship fulfill my core needs?

_____

_____

_____

9. What do I have proof of? Review the list of signs and symptoms that are common to cheaters as detailed in the self-help book, The Truth About The Lies–"If Only I Had Proof," and identify how many you have observed in your man.

_____

_____

_____

10. Admit your man has cheated before and you stayed with a cheater. Can you admit there are signs he is cheating again? Make a list of the signs you clearly see and accept that the choice to stay with him or to leave is yours.

_____

_____

_____

Now, having answered all the questions, what is your truth?

_____

_____

_____

_____

_____

_____

_____

_____

_____

_____

_____

_____

_____

_____

_____

_____

_____

_____

_____

_____

_____

2 ALL MEN ARE CHEATERS

Let's start by challenging a common generalization. All men are not cheaters. All men are susceptible to cheating, but some choose not to cheat. Some men will honor their commitment to their women. There are men who are cheaters, and there are men who have cheated. How the cheater acts and thinks is distinctly different from the man who has cheated. If you want to know whether you are with a cheater or a man who has cheated, do an honest character analysis as described in The Truth About The Lies self-help guide. When you do this, you will get unstuck and determine what you want to do about your cheater.

A cheater will probably always be a cheater, but a man who has cheated will likely be able to repent, reform, and recommit to his woman. His change will be from the inside out and not based solely on emotions. In order to reveal which one you are in a relationship with, stick with the facts and do a fact-based analysis of your man's character and actions. Don't get lost in the haze of irrelevant information, presumptions, and excuses. Do not create scenarios that do not exist. Simply stick with the concrete facts of events and you will see the truth.

To reveal your truth, ask yourself:

1. Did your man confess to a history of cheating? Provide the facts below.

   _____

   _____

   _____

2. Is he able to verbalize what led to his decision to cheat and what led him to stop cheating? Ask him to reveal the depth of his cheating; a one-night stand, a long-term affair, or a series of indiscretions.

   _____

   _____

   _____

3. Is he willing and able to accept all responsibility for his choice to cheat without justifying his actions because his needs were not being met? Is he remorseful?

_____

_____

_____

4. Deal only with the facts and avoid over-analyzing. Don't seek advice from others until you have dealt only with the facts "as is" without generalizing, rationalizing, or minimizing. Don't mix the facts with perceptions, beliefs, or predictions. The facts are simple, clear, and easily seen. List them below.

_____

_____

_____

5. Does your man believe cheating is wrong? Is cheating ever justifiable in his belief system and his value system?

_____

_____

_____

6. In his history of cheating, do you recognize cheating as a default behavior? Examples of cheating as a default are; his needs aren't being met, so he resorts to cheating, he feels misunderstood, so he cheats, he feels unappreciated, so he cheats. Has there been a recurrent pattern of cheating in his relationship history; has he cheated on multiple partners?

_____

_____

_____

2 All Men Are Cheaters

7. Are his boundaries protective of your relationship and his commitment to you, or does he weave in and out, leaving open doors for inappropriate actions and situations to occur?

_____

_____

_____

8. When caught cheating, how did he react? Did he accept responsibility for his actions, and was he humble? Did he seek your forgiveness?

_____

_____

_____

9. Did he seek to justify his cheating by pointing out what you were doing wrong, or what you were failing to do before he had fully accepted responsibility for his choice to cheat?

_____

_____

_____

10. Does he want you to get over the cheating quickly and move on? Does he get irritated and defensive when you ask questions or seek answers?

_____

_____

_____

11. Did you identify cheating as a deal breaker? Does staying with your cheating man violate your boundaries, devalue your worth, or betray your value system?

_____

_____

_____

12. Has your man showed he shares your values and beliefs about cheating? If he cheated on someone else in the past and has cheated on you, are you with a man who has cheated or are you with a cheater?

_____

_____

_____

Now, having answered all the questions, what is your truth?

_____

_____

_____

_____

_____

_____

_____

_____

_____

_____

_____

_____

_____

_____

_____

_____

_____

_____

_____

_____

_____

3   HE CONFESSED SO
HE'S READY TO CHANGE

The best proof of your man's cheating is his confession, but there are levels of confessions. You have the partial confession that consists of part truth and part denial. Then there is the guarded confession that is a mixture of fact and fiction. A true confession is delivered straight with no chaser and reflects the events exactly as they occurred. A confession is admitting involvement, association, and guilt. What a confession is not is a sign of change.

It is easy to see how a confession from your cheating man can render you stuck because of all you choose to read into it. The confession is continuously reviewed, rehashed, replayed, and reprocessed until you give it the meaning you want it to have. The meaning doesn't come from the confession or facts; it comes from your wounds and your needs. What this confession means to you is not necessarily the same as what he intended for it to convey. Because you made the confession mean your man is ready to change, it renders you stuck in the haze of self-created hope waiting for him to stop cheating.

To reveal your truth, you need to review but not revise, replay but not rewrite, and rehash but not repress. A confession can be the first step towards contemplation of change, but the process of change happens over time. A confession does not equate to automatic transformation. The character flaws that allowed the cheating are still alive and active. Just because he was ready to confess doesn't mean he is also ready to change. This is where you will have to develop a strategy to override your emotional reasoning. A system of checks and balances, with consistency in words and actions, should be used to verify his readiness for change.

To reveal your truth, ask yourself:

1. Strip the confession of all of your "add-ons." Remove every assumption you have attached to the confession. Make a list consisting only of the detailed facts of the confession and not the story you have created.

_____

_____

2. You perceive the confession as a sign of his respect for you, and therefore you respect him for confessing. Identify which of his actions, while cheating, you consider respectful. Go back to the facts of the confession and re-evaluate whether you can find evidence of respect for you or a reason to respect him.

_____

_____

_____

3. After the confession, you should be vigilant. Watch for signs of preparation for change. Boundaries should be firm, habits should be changed, and decisions should be consistent. What exactly do you see?

_____

_____

_____

4. Is your man interested in self-examination to gain an understanding of why he cheats? Observe and log his ability to verbalize his genuine needs.

_____

_____

_____

5. It will be important to be honest with yourself about whether your man has developed the ability to challenge his need for immediate gratification. List the evidence that he is now practicing self-discipline.

_____

_____

_____

6. If the confession meant he was ready to stop cheating, you will notice new behaviors and actions. List all new behaviors that are consistent with the changes you expected to see following the confession. Consistency measures commitment to change; without consistency, there is no genuine change. Are his new behaviors consistent?

_____

_____

_____

7. On a scale of 1-10, with 1 being low and 10 being high, rate his level of consistency with the behaviors you have listed.

_____

_____

_____

8. Have his actions lived up to his words? Has he changed or has he simply confessed to cheating?

_____

_____

_____

Now, having answered all the questions, what is your truth?

_____

_____

_____

_____

_____

_____

_____

_____

_____

_____

_____

_____

_____

_____

_____

_____

_____

_____

_____

_____

_____

4 SHE MEANS NOTHING TO HIM

When you are blind, you think about the woman your man is cheating with as nothing more than a mistake. You believe he loves you, so how could "she" be anything other than a mistake? Your blindness leads you to believe you know your man well enough to know this woman is nothing more than the result of his vices being played out. You have acknowledged he has a wondering eye, is flirtatious, and too darn friendly. Despite all this, you are certain your man loves you, and therefore the woman he cheated with is a non-factor in your relationship.

Because you were aware of his vices, you predicted his flirting and friendliness would someday get him into trouble. You haven't developed the vision to see him as a cheater; therefore, your focus is in the wrong place. Instead of seeing him as the cheater he is, you see him as one who has gotten himself into something he could not escape. You have made the other woman a non-factor and decided your energy needs to be focused on helping your man see how he ended up making this mistake. To intensify your blindness, you rake the other woman over the coals to discredit her value.

Your blindness leads you to maintain "she" was his mistake. He didn't cheat on you, he simply made a mistake. Because your focus continues to be in the wrong place, you continue to cloud your vision with faulty beliefs that skew the obvious cheating that has taken place. A play on words turns cheating into just sex, sex into a meaningless activity, and the other woman into a meaningless mistake. You choose to believe she means nothing because he loves you, but choosing to believe she means nothing doesn't make it the truth.

To reveal your truth, ask yourself:

1. Do his actions feel like love and honor you as his woman?

   _____

   _____

   _____

19

2. What makes you the one he loves? What evidence do you have to support his love for you and the other woman's lack of value?

_____

_____

_____

3. Does the time invested in the relationship make you the one he loves and values? Does the belief he loves you stem from the fact that you two are still together?

_____

_____

_____

4. With what measure of dignity are you able to stay with a man who cheated on you with someone who means nothing to him? If he cheats on you with someone who means nothing to him, what does that say about his love for you?

_____

_____

_____

5. Since being caught cheating, has he communicated with the other woman who means nothing to him? What proof do you have that their relationship is over?

_____

_____

_____

6. What does the other woman know about you? If "she" doesn't know you exist, then what do you mean to him?

_____

_____

7. You know about the other woman and see her as your man's mistake. If the other woman knows about you, she possibly considers you to be a factor in your man's misery. Which one of you is right? The most important thing to consider is the fact that having both of you makes him a cheater. Is he really a victim of his vices, or is he a cheater?

_____

_____

_____

8. Do his actions show he cares about the impact his cheating has on your well-being? Does thinking the other woman means nothing to him help you love yourself? How do you show self-love while staying with your cheating man?

_____

_____

_____

9. Whose mistake is the other woman? Is she your mistaken belief, or is she your man's mistaken action?

_____

_____

_____

10. What do you and the other woman share; have in common? Whose man is he?

_____

_____

_____

Now, having answered all the questions, what is your truth?

_____

_____

_____

_____

_____

_____

_____

_____

_____

_____

_____

_____

_____

_____

_____

_____

_____

_____

_____

_____

_____

PART 2

"THE MANIPULATOR"

Gaining sight of your man's cheating will transform you from "The Blind" to "The Manipulator." Changing into "The Manipulator" allows you to cope with his cheating by becoming very skillful at using and altering facts to be consistent with what you need to believe. Your man's cheating becomes a means to an end, a way to get what you want. The lies you tell yourself to manipulate your circumstances into something favorable keep you stuck with him. Sadly, the only one being manipulated is you. To stop this behavior, search for the truth underneath all the lies you have so skillfully crafted in order to stay with him. You will need to acknowledge that your manipulation is not creating what you want in the relationship because you genuinely desire to have a faithful man. Can you admit you cannot manipulate the cheating out of him?

Over time, you have become very skillful at what you create. Not only have you created a way to minimize the primary issue, your man's cheating, you have also elevated the other woman as your focal point. Your ego surges into overdrive, causing you to miss the primary issues which are your man's cheating and him opening you up to being disrespected by both him and his woman. Your ego dashes straight past the primary issues to shine a light on the nerve of the other woman to cheat with your man. Your manipulative spirit has blinded you to the fact that trying to deny her of satisfaction is only blocking your future satisfaction.

The longer you stay, the more manipulative you will have to become to convince yourself you are not wasting your time. You mistakenly believe your actions will have a transformational effect on his cheating. Yes, you have created an unspoken contract with your man that binds him to correct his behavior because you made a choice to stay. The problem is, this is all in your head and not based on facts or actions. Becoming "The Manipulator" gives you a false sense of control and entitlement that will never result in your ability to have what you need, want, and desire from him. As said before, the only one who is being manipulated is you.

5 I'M NOT GOING TO GIVE HER THE SATISFACTION OF ME LEAVING HIM

Normally by the time the other woman makes her presence known, the affair has run its course. Her blinders have come off, and she realizes your man is not leaving you as he may have promised. She now realizes she is being played, she is wasting her time, and she will not replace you. Her primary goal now is to manipulate you, and you fall right into her trap. Ever since she first contacted you, your primary mission has been to make someone who already realizes her insignificance feel insignificant as you choose to stay with your cheating man. While fighting for a false sense of significance, you totally miss the manipulation you are subjecting yourself to by attempting to use the other woman to get what you want from him.

The manipulator in you believes the other woman started something that you're going to finish. You fool yourself into believing you are going to use her to get what you want from him. Are you concerned with your man's cheating? Sure you are, but you are more concerned with proving a point to the other woman by using her to manipulate what you want from him. All you get from your manipulation is the opportunity to wear yourself out plotting and scheming.

To reveal your truth, ask yourself:

1. How did you allow the primary issue, your man's cheating, to dodge the bullet? How did the other woman become your focal point instead of the man who is supposed to be committed to you?

   _____

   _____

   _____

2. Is staying with your cheating man really punishment for the other woman, or are you punishing yourself?

   _____

_____

_____

3. Who is really in control here, you, the other woman, or your cheating man?

    _____

    _____

    _____

4. Is proving a point to the other woman more important than his cheating? Will you ever gain true satisfaction by staying with your man despite his cheating?

    _____

    _____

    _____

5. In the end you will give the other woman a lot of attention in order to prove a point to her, and you will give your man a lot of attention to make him stay away from her. Is this a winning situation for you?

    _____

    _____

    _____

6. The bond you will develop with your cheating man by not giving the other woman the satisfaction of you leaving him is false. Is this what you want?

    _____

    _____

    _____

7. What would you be giving the other woman if you left? Are you really in a position to give to or block anything from her?

    _____

_____

_____

8. Your cheating man gave himself to the other woman, so it is up to him to give himself back to you. Does your decision to stay mean he has given himself back to you?

_____

_____

_____

9. Leaving wouldn't be giving the other woman satisfaction. It would give her a cheating man. Could you gain satisfaction from leaving a relationship that doesn't honor your values rather than staying to prove a point to someone who has no value in your life?

_____

_____

_____

10. Are you staying with your cheating man because you love him or because you want to prove a point? Will staying with him give you a sense of security and peace, or will it keep you vengeful and bitter? Is staying, to avoid giving "her the satisfaction," a good use of your time and energy?

_____

_____

_____

11. When was the last time he was all yours? When he cheated in the past, what satisfaction did you get from staying? Do you believe he will stop cheating this time?

_____

_____

_____

Now, having answered all the questions, what is your truth?

_____

_____

_____

_____

_____

_____

_____

_____

_____

_____

_____

_____

_____

_____

_____

_____

_____

_____

_____

_____

_____

6   IF I STAY HE'LL SEE HOW MUCH
I LOVE HIM AND STOP CHEATING

Your man cheats, you leave him, and he falls to pieces. This is how the drama starts, but it doesn't end there. He professes his love for you by begging, pleading, and maintaining he cannot imagine living without you. You remain unforgiving, and the drama continues. He persists and stalks you, hoping you will give in and take him back. You mistake all his actions as a sign of him being ready to change and decide to give him another chance. You convince yourself the act of taking him back will show your deep, undying love, and he will stop cheating. In your mind, this drama ends with the two of you living happily ever after.

The biggest misconception in this lie is the fact you think your actions can control his behaviors. You think your demonstration of love will result in his demonstration of change, and he will stop cheating. He manipulated you into staying with him and you intend to manipulate him into no longer cheating. Your choice to stay with him after he cheated is not an act of love; it is an act of control. To choose to stay with him unconditionally, with no hidden expectations of future gain, would be an act of love. Becoming "The Manipulator" and using an act of control to symbolize love will never end in genuine love. A more beneficial use of your energy would be to spend some time separating the truth from the lies.

To reveal your truth, ask yourself:

1. You believe staying with him after he has cheated will show how much you love him. Did he see how much you loved him before and during the cheating? Did that stop his cheating?

   _____

   _____

   _____

2. Your man cheated before and you stayed. Why would staying this time make him see anything differently? Are you attaching a quality of love that he will see to the quantity of

times you put up with his cheating? Do you believe the following equations; the more he cheats + the longer I stay = how much I love him, and for him; the more I cheat + the longer she stays = I see her love and stop cheating?

_____

_____

_____

3. What do you envision doing, saying, and giving to keep his affections in the relationship, and how much are you willing to do?

_____

_____

_____

4. Are you truly committed to making the relationship better? What would make you feel your cheating man is worthy of the efforts you are making to show your love?

_____

_____

_____

5. What went wrong before when you stayed? Did you not express your love enough for him to stop cheating? Did he mistake you staying as a pass to continue to cheat because you didn't leave?

_____

_____

_____

6. Is your love for him growing with each discovery of cheating?

_____

_____

7. When would you have done enough to prove to him how much you love him?

_____

_____

_____

8. Are you being your true self or trying to become who you think he wants?

_____

_____

_____

9. Love grows from security, authenticity, and congruency. Do you believe love can also grow from scheming, manipulating, and calculating?

_____

_____

_____

10. Will you be able to genuinely love someone you cannot trust?

_____

_____

_____

11. Are the scales balanced? While you show him how much you love him, is he doing the same? While you give more, is he doing the same? Does he appreciate your love for him, and do you feel loved by him?

_____

_____

_____

Now, having answered all the questions, what is your truth?

_____

_____

_____

_____

_____

_____

_____

_____

_____

_____

_____

_____

_____

_____

_____

_____

_____

_____

_____

_____

7 BECAUSE I STAYED AFTER HE CHEATED AGAIN HE OWES ME

Some women believe they can love the cheating right out of their men by staying after he cheats. That's not your belief at all. You choose to believe your man's cheating has created a debt for him to repay you for staying, and that debt is his fidelity. Your manipulative mind has caused you to connect your choice to stay with his duty to change. The trouble with this belief is your man is the only one who can decide to stop cheating, and his decision has nothing to do with your choice to stay. You have created a debt for him to pay for his cheating, but it is totally up to him to decide whether he intends to honor the debt by being faithful.

Getting unstuck will require you to peel back the layers of this lie to get down to the core. The core is the facts, unaltered by your perceptions. The core is also an honest assessment of his actions, choices, and character. After you have looked at the facts and have done an honest assessment, you will find the truth at the core. The truth will reveal to you what more than likely will happen in the future with your cheating man. The truth will enlighten you to the fact that the one who owes you something is you, and you will repay yourself with honesty.

To reveal your truth, ask yourself:

1. If your man wasn't consistent and didn't commit to doing what it took to keep you after the first time he cheated, what makes you think he will do anything differently this time?

   _____

   _____

   _____

2. Will your choice to stay with him result in you having the man you want? Will staying make him value his relationship with you to the point of never putting himself in a position to lose you?

   _____

_____

_____

3. Is your purpose for staying with him to heal your wounds and work on developing a deeper level of love? How will you be able to restore your trust in him?

_____

_____

_____

4. Will your choice to stay result in him valuing you enough to do what it takes to make you feel secure in the relationship?

_____

_____

_____

5. Is your motivation to stay sparked by negative or positive energy? Is it possible to turn your belief in his need to redeem himself into a healthy reconciliation?

_____

_____

_____

6. How has this current act of cheating created the opportunity for you to get what you want? Has he honored your list of wants, needs, and desires in the past?

_____

_____

_____

7. By staying, are you seeking restoration and repair of what's damaged, or control of what you want through commands and demands? What does he have to gain from you staying?

_____

_____

_____

8. Does the fact that he cheated, and you stayed, create an entirely new relationship? Have the two of you changed? Are you hoping to manufacture a relationship where he doesn't cheat because he is thinking about what you need and not about what he wants?

_____

_____

_____

9. Are you staying because you want to make all he has put you through worth your investment in the relationship? Will you feel the additional investment was worth your time, even if he cheats again?

_____

_____

_____

10. What will you do when he decides he doesn't owe you anything and reverts to his old ways? Will you then be ready to face the truth about your relationship?

_____

_____

_____

11. Will your choice to stay give you more control or make you feel more out of control? Will staying give you the security you seek, or will it magnify the insecurities the relationship has created?

_____

_____

_____

12. Will his cheating be acceptable, and would you be able to forgive, if he acts as if he owes you for staying?

_____

_____

_____

13. Does he owe you for his cheating or you staying? What would he actually have to do to make you feel the debt he owes you has been paid?

_____

_____

_____

Now, having answered all the questions, what is your truth?

_____

_____

_____

_____

_____

_____

_____

_____

_____

_____

_____

_____

_____

_____

_____

_____

_____

_____

_____

_____

_____

PART 3

"THE FINGER-POINTER"

It is easier to accept inappropriate behavior from your man if you can make someone else responsible. When your level of denial is elevated, and you can't see past the perpetrators you blame for your man's behaviors, you have become "The Finger-Pointer." You have perfected the craft of finding someone or something else to blame for why he cheats. You choose to see him as the victim of circumstances and not responsible for his cheating. The problem with this lie is he will never change because he's not expected to, not thought to be capable of, and not held responsible for change. Everyone and everything else around him needs to change, and then your poor little helpless cheater will have the support he needs to be faithful.

There is no shortage of circumstances and people to blame for your man's cheating, and therefore change will never come. If he cheats because of how he was raised, who he hangs around, because other women proposition him, or a host of other reasons you continue to pull out of your hat, then he gets to keep cheating. Every time he cheats, your finger extends in a new direction, but it never points to the common denominator in all the cheating. You gloss over the fact that this grown man continues to make immature choices, and you bail him out by locking your sites on secondary factors to his cheating. Sure he has cheaters in his family, he has friends who cheat, and he has women coming after him, but his cheating is his choice. To get unstuck you will have to face the fact that your man cheats because of his choices, not because he is a victim. Your finger-pointing is keeping you stuck with what you don't want, and that is a cheating man.

8 HE CHEATS BECAUSE OF
HOW HE WAS RAISED

This lie is like a first glance. If you glance at something, it looks different than it would after you have looked at it more intensely. If you do not look long enough at the details, the first glance will not be a complete illustration of reality. When looking at a parent and observing their flaws, it is easy to understand how the children may have picked up their bad habits. Children learn from observation and imitation, and the primary caretakers are often who they emulate. At first glance, it makes sense that your man cheats because he comes from a long line of cheaters. Take it all in and apply it as you wish, but your man is not an impressionable child, he is an adult.

Observing the facts you have gathered that lead you to point the finger away from your man will provide a character analysis of him. If you apply the facts to him, and not the person you are pointing the finger towards, you will see him clearly. Choosing to point the finger at his family upbringing takes your focus totally off the true perpetrator of his cheating; him. He was created in the image of cheaters, but that does not mean he had to remain the same person throughout his lifespan. The fact that he continues to cheat is evidence that he has continued to honor an image, and his choices, not his upbringing, are the reason he cheats. At some point he has to choose to grow, and until then, you have to admit you are with a grown boy who chooses to cheat.

To reveal your truth, ask yourself:

1. You believe your man cheats because as a child he was continuously exposed to cheaters. As an adult, there is no doubt he has been continuously exposed to men who don't cheat. Why hasn't this changed his behavior, and why has he not attempted to emulate the faithful men?

   _____

   _____

   _____

2. Does your man take accountability for his actions in other areas of his life such as work and community? Why do you think his cheating is different; an unconscious choice he cannot control because of how he was raised?

    _____

    _____

    _____

3. His father, grandfather, and great-grandfather cheated, so it makes sense to you he also cheats. Does his history make his cheating acceptable?

    _____

    _____

    _____

4. If your man cheats because of how he was raised, and has cheated in all his relationships, isn't it clear that cheating is an acceptable part of his value system? If he does not change his value system, will it be hard for him to change his behaviors?

    _____

    _____

    _____

5. You believe your man cheats because of how he was raised. How has your attitude or beliefs enabled him to continue to cheat?

    _____

    _____

    _____

6. Have you ever asked him if he thinks cheating is wrong, unacceptable, or inappropriate?

    _____

    _____

7. Has he ever been in an exclusive, mutually monogamous relationship?

_____

_____

_____

8. When exactly did he share his family and personal history of cheating? Was it before or after he cheated? Under what circumstances did you have the conversation? Did your man point the finger at his upbringing as the reason he cheated or did you?

_____

_____

_____

9. Are you staying with him because you believe he wants to change or because you believe you can change him?

_____

_____

_____

10. Change doesn't happen overnight. How long are you willing to wait for him to change his cheating ways? Are you able to adjust your value system to make cheating acceptable as long as he professes his desire to change?

_____

_____

_____

Now, having answered all the questions, what is your truth?

_____

_____

_____

_____

_____

_____

_____

_____

_____

_____

_____

_____

_____

_____

_____

_____

_____

_____

_____

_____

_____

9   HE CHEATS BECAUSE HE'S INFLUENCED BY HIS FRIENDS

Because you are "The Finger-Pointer" you will have no shortage of external influences for your man's cheating. You will blame his upbringing, his environment, and his friends for his behavior. The problem is you never actually acknowledge that he chooses to cheat, and you grant him an exemption from being held accountable for his choices and actions. Instead of seeing him as a grown man who can make his own decisions, you choose to see him as a victim of circumstances, and you point the finger in another direction.

You were excited when he introduced you to his friends. Many women feel this act reflects a priority status in her man's life, a gesture that signifies a serious relationship. Meeting his friends meant he wanted to share his life with you and make you a part of his future. Meeting his friends was considered a privilege until you got to know them. After meeting them, you vowed to do nothing short of rescue your man from their influences. Your perception led you to conclude his friends' negative habits would inevitably have a negative influence on your innocent man.

This lie will keep you stuck with your cheating man until he has no friends for you to blame. This will be the only thing that would force you to see he alone has been the source of his cheating. Even if he became a loner, your finger would probably continue to point in the wrong direction. Your pattern of denial would blame the lingering effects of hanging with cheaters as the reason he continues to cheat. Looking only at him, as an individual capable of making independent decisions, is the path to the truth.

To reveal your truth, ask yourself:

1. Does it bother your man that his friends cheat?

   _____

   _____

   _____

2. Does he lie for his friends by creating and being a part of the alibis they tell their women?

_____

_____

_____

3. Does he think cheating is wrong? Have you ever witnessed him disagree with a friend's decision to cheat? Has he ever discouraged a friend from involving him in his alibis?

_____

_____

_____

4. If you see his friends as cheaters, liars, and corrupt, and you believe birds of a feather flock together, then what does that make your man? How do you think his friends women see him?

_____

_____

_____

5. If your man is comfortable with the lies he tells for his friends, does that make him a liar? Is it safe to say your man is comfortable playing games?

_____

_____

_____

6. You say your man cheats because he doesn't want to look weak to his friends. Is it ok with you that he doesn't mind looking dishonest and unfaithful to you?

_____

_____

_____

7. Your man would rather his friends see him as one of them, and that is why you say he cheats. Is it possible they see him as one of them because he is one of them?

_____

_____

_____

8. You believe his friends pressured him into cheating. On the flip side, you were trying to pressure him into not cheating. Why did he fall prey to their pressure and not yours?

_____

_____

_____

9. Why do you want to continue in a relationship with a grown man who cannot make independent decisions about his actions?

_____

_____

_____

10. Why would you ever entrust your heart to a man who allows his friends to dictate his actions?

_____

_____

_____

11. Do you want to spend your time babysitting your man's moral compass to discourage him from cheating, or would you rather be with a man who naturally thinks cheating is morally wrong?

_____

_____

12. What do you want compared to what you already have? Describe what you have on one side of a piece of paper, then flip it over and write what you want. Compare the two lists. Are you getting what you want, and are your needs being met?

_____

_____

_____

Now, having answered all the questions, what is your truth?

_____

_____

_____

_____

_____

_____

_____

_____

_____

_____

_____

_____

_____

_____

_____

_____

_____

_____

_____

_____

_____

_____

10 HE CHEATED BECAUSE
SHE CAME AFTER HIM

Your man cheats and you point your finger in the opposite direction, at the other woman. In your finger-pointing state of denial he cheated because she came after him, and he could not resist the temptation, but not because he's a cheater. Your rationale is he would not have cheated if she had not come after him. You have given your man a golden pass to cheat because, "A man will be a man."

How long will you continue to believe he cheated solely because the other woman came after him? Even though he took the time to remove his clothes and lay down with her, you believe he only cheated because she came after him. I suppose this woman had him spellbound and incapable of thinking. You never once considered that he chose to cheat. You have blocked the possibility that he cheated because he could and because he wanted to from entering your tunnel vision. Your way of thinking allows him to continue to cheat, and he couldn't care less who you blame for his choice as long as the finger continues to point away from him.

You are a smart woman, and you know it takes two to create the atmosphere, the circumstances, and the culmination of an affair. The lie he cheated because the other woman came after him keeps you stuck with a cheater. Because you will not address the role he plays in the cheating, the scales are never balanced. It places all the weight on the other woman, and he is free of any responsibility to change. Until you balance the scales and stop hiding from the truth, you will be stuck with your cheating man.

To reveal your truth, ask yourself:

1. You blame the other woman for your man's cheating, but she wasn't in a relationship with you. Who is really to blame for the cheating that interrupted your relationship? Who owes you their loyalty, your man or the other woman?

_____

_____

_____

2. You acknowledge that your man wasn't able to resist the other woman when she came after him. If he resisted her, wouldn't you say he was responsible for not cheating? Shouldn't he be held accountable and responsible on both ends of the spectrum?

_____

_____

_____

3. If he allows you to blame the other woman, and he in turn tells you what you weren't doing that led him to cheat, is he making you responsible for his cheating? How is it he will point the finger at you, but you won't point it at him?

_____

_____

_____

4. If your man blames you for his cheating and you blame the other woman, what motivation is there for him to change? How does your choice to blame the other woman help your relationship with him? Does blaming the other woman help you trust him?

_____

_____

_____

5. Your man could have gotten his needs met in other ways, but he cheated. Why do you choose to believe his cheating was not a conscious choice? Are his actions showing you that cheating is the only way he knows how to get his needs met?

_____

_____

_____

6. You believe your man cheated only because the other woman came after him. Does this mean he cannot set healthy boundaries that protect his commitment to you? Has he shown you he can set boundaries that will support a monogamous relationship?

_____

_____

_____

7. There are always signs that sexual tension is building. Does your man know the difference between what is appropriate and inappropriate in a committed relationship?

_____

_____

_____

8. How long has cheating been a factor in your relationship? How many women has he cheated with? Do you have proof that they all came after him?

_____

_____

_____

9. Just because the other woman came after him doesn't automatically mean he had to cheat. Are you able to conceptualize the fact that your man saw her coming and met her halfway? Are you able to process the possibility that the two of them jointly decided to cheat?

_____

_____

_____

10. If you choose to continue to point the finger at the other woman, how will this prompt your man to reassess his choices?

_____

_____

_____

11. Does the fact that your man allowed you to point the finger at the other woman raise any red flags for you? What does his comfort with you coming after the other woman tell you about his character?

_____

_____

_____

12. Usually the person who stands back and allows others to take the blame for their actions does not change inappropriate or unacceptable behaviors. Do you believe this is true of your cheating man?

_____

_____

_____

Now, having answered all the questions, what is your truth?

_____

_____

_____

_____

_____

_____

_____

_____

_____

_____

_____

_____

_____

_____

_____

_____

_____

_____

_____

_____

_____

11 HE CHEATED BECAUSE I _____
(FILL IN THE BLANK)

As long as you are busy pointing the finger away from your man, he will continue to cheat. It does not matter whether you are blaming yourself or pointing the finger at someone else, he will gladly step aside and let the blame fall where it may. Almost anyone or anything will do as long as you can continue to deceive yourself into believing his cheating is not by choice. Your denial keeps you from holding him responsible for his actions, and you point the finger at yourself as the cause of his cheating.

There is no shortage of reasons you will identify to fill in the blank for why your man cheats. You choose to believe if you did a little more of this and a little less of that, he would stop cheating. All it takes is a little more thinking and a lot less blaming to put this lie to rest. If what you did had the power to control him, surely you would use that power to stop his cheating. You wholeheartedly believe his cheating is caused by you and not by him.

Your man is more than happy to allow you to take the blame for his cheating. He is so gracious he even helps you to recognize your faults and flaws that cause him to cheat. Each time you catch him crossing a boundary line or violating your trust, he points the finger at you and dishes out a hefty dose of blame. He blames you, you accept the blame, and he continues to cheat. This vicious cycle could go on forever if you are not willing to tell yourself the truth. You beat yourself down and allow him to take you on a guilt trip each time he cheats because you are too scared to face the truth about the lies you have created to protect him from being responsible for his cheating.

To reveal your truth, ask yourself:

1. You take full credit for doing or not doing things that influence your man to cheat. Can you turn this around and use that same influence to make him stop cheating?

   _____

   _____

2. Why haven't you been able to nullify his cheating in the same way you claim to have caused him to cheat? Could it be because you really have no control over his choice to cheat?

_____

_____

_____

3. How do his words convict you of being responsible for his cheating?

_____

_____

_____

4. Does his cheating mean you have failed as his woman, or does it mean he has failed as your man?

_____

_____

_____

5. Could it be he cheated because he does not share the same values as you?

_____

_____

_____

6. Does the reason for his cheating remain consistent, or does it keep changing? What happens when you try to fix the things that you have been doing/not doing?

_____

_____

_____

7. If your actions caused him to cheat, that means he went out seeking to have an affair. Does that make him responsible for his actions? If you fill in the blank with, "He cheated because he went out looking for an affair," would this make him responsible for his cheating?

_____

_____

_____

8. Is it possible to fix what is broken if you don't have the proper tools? What is broken is his ability to be faithful because it's the right thing to do. Can you change his values?

_____

_____

_____

9. If his default action is to cheat when his needs are not being met, what does that make him? What does that say about his character?

_____

_____

_____

10. Wouldn't you rather be with a man who does not cheat because of who he is and not because of what you do? Can you fix it so his default is set on honesty, commitment, and respect instead of cheating?

_____

_____

_____

Now, having answered all the questions, what is your truth?

_____

_____

_____

_____

_____

_____

_____

_____

_____

_____

_____

_____

_____

_____

_____

_____

_____

_____

_____

PART 4

"THE DREAMER"

When you abandon your better judgment and start thinking as "The Dreamer," you clearly see your man is cheating. Unlike the woman who copes by manipulation, you are not interested in using his cheating to your advantage. You are also not like the woman who points her finger to blame everyone and everything for her man's cheating. In your dreams you see the wonderful illusion of potential, which blinds you from seeing the truth. In order to cope with his cheating, you live partially in reality and partially in your dreams.

Dreams are based on what you desire, and you choose to believe he will change after some event in the future. You would rather take a chance and believe he will stop cheating rather than deal with the reality that he is a cheater. There is no denying he is cheating, but you are not ready to call him a cheater. If you accepted that, there would be no foundation for your dreams. That would force you to abandon the dream and accept the truth. Instead, you stay stuck with a cheater while dreaming of better days.

Probably one of the most common dreams is a cheater will change after he marries. In your dreams, marriage is perceived as being capable of clarifying his values. If marriage doesn't get the job done, then surely having a baby will do the trick. Many dreamers have climbed out on a limb hoping for a miracle with the birth of a child only to be shaken back to reality. If you can't talk your man into changing, hopefully a professional can make him change. A counselor is skilled at dealing with cheaters, and you dream counseling will transform his mind into that of a faithful man. Then there is the ultimate dream, believing in the power of attending church to change him. Your dream is he will change after _____. As long as you can come up with reasons to fill in the blank, your dream will live on, and you will stay stuck with your cheater.

12 HE'LL CHANGE AFTER
WE GET MARRIED

Despite broken promises, half-truths, and inconsistencies, you and your man have weathered the storms of infidelity. You tied a knot at the end of your rope when you did not think you could hold on any longer, and now you intend to tie the knot with your cheating man. You believe being single and independent are the reasons he continues to cheat. In your dreams, after the two of you get married, he will stop cheating. Because you've hung in there through hell and high water, you believe you've earned the right to the title of "Mrs.," and to be repaid with marriage.

Let's review the facts. You caught him cheating. He has not stopped cheating since being caught, but he toned it down a bit. This gives you hope he will change totally after you get married. You see his potential and believe marriage will help him continue to become a committed partner. The fact is, potential is not change. Marrying him keeps you stuck with a man who has the potential to stop cheating. You are choosing to marry a cheater.

To reveal your truth, ask yourself:

1. You say he has changed. Has he changed enough to provide you with the sense of security you seek in a husband?

   _____

   _____

   _____

2. Has he changed enough to increase your level of trust in him and to show you he has your best interest at heart?

   _____

   _____

   _____

3. You believe marriage changes people, and people change because of marriage. What behaviors has he shown that make you believe he will change after marriage?

_____

_____

_____

4. What inappropriate behaviors are you now accepting? Will marrying him set you up to accept even more?

_____

_____

_____

5. Why should he change after you get married if he cheated before the marriage, and you married him anyway?

_____

_____

_____

6. Marriage is not a piece of paper; it is a state of mind. Your man has shown he values cheating over monogamy. Will marriage automatically change his value system?

_____

_____

_____

7. One of the most important factors in having a successful marriage is choosing the right person for you. Does your man have the "potential" to be the right person for you, or is he the right person for you "as is?"

_____

_____

8. Successful marriages require two people committing to the same values and principles. Marriage is a mindset, a covenant, and a union. Do you two share the same mindset and commitment that sets the appropriate boundaries to support being faithful?

_____

_____

_____

9. Are you expecting marriage to transform his character and be a remedy for cheating?

_____

_____

_____

10. Marriage is a binding contract that comes with a set of expectations. Have you and he agreed upon the expectations and boundaries that will govern your marital relationship?

_____

_____

_____

11. Are you marrying the man or the expectations of the vows?

_____

_____

_____

12. If you believe he has the potential to change, and he will change after marriage, why not wait until he actually changes before getting married?

_____

_____

_____

Now, having answered all the questions, what is your truth?

13 HE'LL CHANGE AFTER
WE HAVE A CHILD

If you hold on to an illusion long enough, it will turn into a delusion. An illusion can trick you and lead to false or misleading perceptions. A relationship illusion is seeing your man as a faithful partner but refocusing to realize he is still a cheater. A delusion is different. It leads you to believe something is possible despite the obvious reality to the contrary. With delusions you are persistently altering your reality, and this happens as you become "The Dreamer." Your man has entered the marriage but failed to commit to your expectations and the traditional boundaries that follow "I Do." You acknowledge he is still cheating but cannot admit he cheats because he is a cheater. The illusion of him having the potential to change is turning into a delusion and keeps you stuck with him.

The holy Bible states, "Faith is the essence of things hoped for," and you use this belief to anchor your hope that he will change after you have children. Anchors are heavy and hard to move, and so is your belief in his potential to become a faithful man. You continue to keep hope alive despite the obvious signs that he continues to cheat, and you become stuck in a dream world where potential is reality and reality is ignored. Believing in something despite evidence to the contrary makes you delusional not hopeful. To get unstuck you will have to challenge the blossoming delusional belief that children will change your man's cheating ways.

To reveal your truth, ask yourself:

1. Having children will move you and your cheating man from being a couple to being a family. Are you expecting the titles of family and father to change his cheating ways? For a frame of reference, did the titles of couple or partner stop his cheating?

   _____

   _____

   _____

2. Sometimes becoming a parent shifts a man's values in the right direction, but there is a difference between being a partner and being a father. Isn't it possible that he will value being a father and still not value being a faithful partner?

    _____

    _____

    _____

3. What makes you believe his love for a baby will trickle down to you?

    _____

    _____

    _____

4. You believe having a baby will make your man appreciate you. Has he shown any evidence of appreciation for you as his woman? Did he appreciate you before you got pregnant?

    _____

    _____

    _____

5. He doesn't share your values for being in a committed relationship, so what makes you believe having a child will cause him to share your values and no longer cheat?

    _____

    _____

    _____

6. Reflect on your knowledge of men continuing to cheat after having children and having children with multiple women. How many men do you know personally who have changed as a partner because of becoming fathers? Did that change include becoming faithful to their women?

    _____

_____

_____

7. Think about the reality of men leaving woman after having children. Are there any indicators that this could be your reality?

    _____

    _____

    _____

8. How can you, as his woman, be emotionally secure in a relationship with a man who is committed to the child and not you?

    _____

    _____

    _____

9. Are you attempting to use having a child to accomplish what you could not in the past? Is having a child your way of increasing the odds of him changing? What would life look like if you embraced the truth of your current relationship?

    _____

    _____

    _____

10. Do you envision him no longer staying out late and hanging out less often because he has a child? Will this belief lead you to intertwine your needs with what you will profess as the child's needs? For example, would you say the child misses daddy when he's not home, or the child deserves to spend more time with daddy?

    _____

    _____

    _____

Now, having answered all the questions, what is your truth?

_____

_____

_____

_____

_____

_____

_____

_____

_____

_____

_____

_____

_____

_____

_____

_____

_____

_____

_____

14 HE'LL CHANGE AFTER WE GO TO COUNSELING

Is it a dream to think your man will change after the two of you go to counseling and to believe counseling has the power to change him? Counseling is an effective tool to assist couples who are ready for change, and it can help them develop the insight and skills to begin the process. It is only effective if those seeking counseling are serious and committed to change. If your man is not ready to change, counseling will be a waste of your time and energy. Also, if he is only going to counseling to satisfy your request, it will not result in consistent change.

After being betrayed, it is normal for you to sort through the hurt, pain, and confusion. It is typical to suggest counseling as a mechanism for healing. You have lots of questions, and your image of him is tarnished. However, the dreamer in you abandons reality and believes bringing your man to a counselor will lead to him becoming an honest, insightful, and thoughtful man who will provide the comfort and security you need to heal. In your dreams, you believe bringing him to counseling will provide the answers to all your questions. You delude yourself into believing he will gain insight into why he cheats, and this will lead to sharing your way into clarity as the counseling process magically changes him. Only in your dreams will this happen, and this delusion has kept you stuck with your cheating man.

An alternative to dragging your unmotivated man into counseling would be for you to use counseling to process information that keeps you stuck with him. You should opt to use counseling to assist with enhancing your insight into how you can make healthy changes that will support your boundaries. Counseling can assist you with accepting the responsibility for actions that have kept you in "dreamland" instead of accepting the truth about his cheating. Counseling or no counseling, he will not change unless he wants to change.

To reveal your truth, ask yourself:

1. In counseling, you expect your man to be totally honest and forthcoming about all his dirt, to understand fully how badly he hurt you, and to be ready to conform to meet all

your needs. What about the counseling process leads you to expect this miracle?

_____

_____

_____

2. His cheating has left you devastated, confused, and humiliated. You feel empty because the cheating cut you to the core and gutted you like a fish. What could he say in counseling to heal these wounds?

_____

_____

_____

3. You believe counseling will help you get the answers to the questions that keep you up at night to include; "who was she," "when did it start," "how long did it go on," "where and how did they meet," "how many times did they have sex," "where did they have sex," and "does he love her," to name a few. Once you have the answers, will it settle your mind, or will the answers cause more anxious fantasies about their relationship?

_____

_____

_____

4. Are you expecting counseling to reform his thinking, transform his values, and enlightened him to the difference between right and wrong?

_____

_____

_____

5. Most women find comfort in talking things through and understanding why things happen; men usually do not. What will you do when he grows tired of answering questions and tells you to, "get over it and move on?" How will you respond when he

blames your lingering need to rehash the past as your source of pain and dismisses his cheating as the cause of the problem?

_____

_____

_____

6. You enter counseling razor focused on the details of his cheating, seeking more answers, more details, and more confessions. Are you using counseling to have a third-party ask the questions you were afraid to ask, challenge the inconsistencies you were afraid to challenge, and get the answers you want to hear?

_____

_____

_____

7. Are you with a cheater (a man with a default behavior that is set on cheating, who has cheated on you before, and who has a history of cheating), or are you with a man who has cheated (one who has not cheated on you before and does not have a history of cheating, but has made a bad decision and cheated this one time)?

_____

_____

_____

8. Is your man going to counseling for you, or is he taking part in counseling with you?

_____

_____

_____

9. Does he believe he can benefit from counseling and want to gain a deeper understanding of why he cheated, or is he using counseling to point out the flaws in you and the relationship to justify his cheating?

_____

_____

_____

10. Does he show sensitivity to your feelings and remorse for causing you such pain? Is he open to answering all your questions, or is he tired of answering the same questions and frustrated by your pain?

_____

_____

_____

11. Is your man going to counseling with you so you can get over his cheating, or is he taking part in counseling as a means of personal growth? Is he motivated to repair what he has damaged, or does he seek to patch up the holes and keep it moving?

_____

_____

_____

12. Is he more focused on you changing and pointing out your flaws than accepting responsibility for his cheating? Does he blame his cheating on you not meeting his needs?

_____

_____

_____

13. Does he see counseling as a waste of time and a means of keeping negativity alive? Does he blame counseling for keeping the two of you stuck and making things worse?

_____

_____

_____

Now, having answered all the questions, what is your truth?

_____

_____

_____

_____

_____

_____

_____

_____

_____

_____

_____

_____

_____

_____

_____

_____

_____

_____

_____

_____

_____

_____

15 HE'LL CHANGE AFTER
HE RECOMMITS TO THE CHURCH

There are few things in the world that outshine the spiritual, mystical, and magical powers associated with the church. Many wayward men have been dragged to church for repentance, and transformation. In your dreams, getting your cheating man to recommit to the church will inevitably lead him to change his ways. All he needs to do is attend church weekly, listen intently, and apply the word to his sinful life. With this equation, change is certain once he recommits to the church.

By attaching to this dream, you have shifted your focus away from the cheating and directed your attention to the act of attending church. If being committed to the church had the power to take away the urge to cheat, we wouldn't hear about pastors cheating. If listening to the sermons had the power to transform cheating ways, then everyone in the church would be faithful to their partners. The church would be a dreamland where all couples would be shielded from infidelity and betrayal because of their commitment to the church.

Do not get it twisted, men can commit to the church and not to their partners. A commitment to the church could lead to acts of service and regular attendance. It could even lead to a desire to live a more righteous life. Being committed to a church could mean holding a position and fulfilling the duties and responsibilities associated with that post. Reconnecting to the church means he commits to the church in some capacity, and that has no connection to his relationship with you. Believing in the dream that your man will stop cheating after he recommits to the church will simply keep you stuck with a cheater who is recommitted to the church and not committed to you.

To reveal your truth, ask yourself:

1. You believe if your man recommits to the church he will change. Has he said he wants to change or showed he feels change is necessary?

_____

_____

2. Change comes from within the person, not from within a building. What is the magic formula for recommitting to the church? Is there a certain number of weeks or a certain number of sermons he needs to attend before being officially recommitted to the church?

_____

_____

_____

3. If your man misses a few church services or does not attend bible study, how do you feel that will influence his cheating?

_____

_____

_____

4. Who determines when he is recommitted to the church: you, him, the pastor, or God?

_____

_____

_____

5. Is church attendance mandatory for him to change? Will there be no hope for him to change if he does not recommit to the church?

_____

_____

_____

6. Do you believe every man who is committed to the church is faithful to his woman?

_____

_____

7. Since you started supervising his church attendance, have you noticed any changes in his thinking and behavior? Does he appear to be more spiritually minded?

_____

_____

_____

8. Is it possible your man will commit to the church but not commit to being faithful to you?

_____

_____

_____

9. What makes you think a mandate to attend church will bring about internal change?

_____

_____

_____

10. There are many news stories about pastors cheating. If the man delivering the sermon is prone to cheat, why would recommitting to church stop your man from cheating?

_____

_____

_____

11. Thinking about, preparing to, and actually changing are all separate phases of the change process. Does your cheating man appear to be in either of these phases?

_____

_____

_____

Now, having answered all the questions, what is your truth?

_____

_____

_____

_____

_____

_____

_____

_____

_____

_____

_____

_____

_____

_____

_____

_____

_____

_____

_____

PART 5

"THE HELPLESS"

To be helpless means being unable to control something, unable to protect oneself, or unable to make a situation better. That is exactly how you, as "The Helpless," cope with your man's cheating. You believe things are happening to you instead of accepting the fact that you are allowing things you don't agree with to happen. There is plenty you could do, but you choose to focus on what you perceive as barriers. This keeps you stuck with your cheating man.

The truth you fail to acknowledge is the fact that you, not your cheating man, are the author of your fate. You are in control even when you choose not to act in your own favor. Choosing to be helpless is not authentic helplessness. Choosing to be helpless is an act of sabotage, and what you are sabotaging is your own happiness. To start believing you can change your circumstances, shift your focus to the things that are in your control. Doing so will strengthen your insight of your self-imposed limitations and ultimately free you from being stuck with him.

Your primary focus has been on what you don't want, and this has weakened your ability to connect to what you want. You want to be with a man who does not cheat, but you have focused on things that will keep you stuck with your cheater. If you believe he is all you have, and you do not want to lose him, then you will never be with the faithful man you truly desire. If you repeatedly tell yourself you do not want to start over, then you have no choice but to stay stuck with him. If you have to stay broken and visibly hurt for him to stop cheating, then you will never have the strength to leave. Because you stayed focused on what you do not want, you give into the lie that being with a cheater is your fate. This lie will make you feel stuck.

16 HE'S ALL I GOT /
I DON'T WANT TO LOSE HIM

If you have come to the point in your relationship where you feel your cheating man is all you have, and you do not want to lose him, you have entered a restrictive mental trap. You have lost yourself in his world by continuously compromising, sacrificing, and abandoning your own values, needs, and boundaries to make him stop cheating. At the point where you have mentally trapped yourself into thinking he is all you have, you have given away so much of yourself it actually feels like he is all you have. You worked so hard to keep him; it is understandable you would not want to lose him.

He is all you have because in your attempts to make him stop cheating you have neglected friendships, strayed away from hobbies, and stood against family in order to monitor him. You have masked your helplessness by over-functioning in the relationship. To safeguard your relationship, you sacrificed your emotional health, which left a void that made you feel he is all you have. The mental trap you created makes you believe if you were to lose him, you would have nothing. Helplessly, you are left feeling like he is all that you've got, and you do not want to lose him because you have given your all to keep him in your life.

To reveal your truth, do these things:

1. You choose to believe your man is all you have because you have lost yourself in his world. List the things you have sacrificed, abandoned, and compromised to continue to exist in his world.

   _____

   _____

   _____

2. Take a moment to revisit your own world; the world you abandoned to keep your man. Make a list of your core relationship boundaries, your core values, and your core needs?

_____

_____

_____

3. Using the two lists above, write down how you have abandoned your own core relationship boundaries, your core values, and your core needs. This should enhance your insight into why you now feel your cheating man is all you have.

_____

_____

_____

4. Next, let's take a look at what you have neglected to continue to exist in his world. How have you neglected your friendships? What hobbies have you neglected in order to spend more time with him? Have you alienated yourself from family in order to block him from going places without you?

_____

_____

_____

5. After learning about his cheating, who jumped into fix-it mode, you or him? Did you start over-functioning to safeguarding the relationship to the point of abandoning your own world and engulfing yourself in his?

_____

_____

_____

6. What has he abandoned, sacrificed, or neglected in order to keep you?

_____

_____

7. Do you agree that the statement, "He's all I got/I don't want to lose him," can be interpreted as, "I have abandoned myself and no longer know who I am?"

_____

_____

_____

8. Have you made his needs become your primary responsibility and pleasing him your primary goal?

_____

_____

_____

9. When did he become all you have? How and why did he become all you have?

_____

_____

_____

10. The devastation caused by the cheating is an indescribable ache, a surreal pain, and an incomprehensible shock one prays will go away. Are you holding on to him attempting to mend the wounds rather than completely tearing away to avoid leaving a gaping hole?

_____

_____

_____

11. How does his cheating enhance your self-image, your self-worth, and your self-confidence?

_____

_____

_____

12. Does staying with your cheating man as "all you got" help you understand who you are? Does what you mean to him make you who you are? Are you looking to him to redefine your worth?

_____

_____

_____

13. Are you consumed with doubt? Have you given him and this relationship the task of redefining and reconstructing you?

_____

_____

_____

14. It is rare to recoup all your losses when an investment loses value? You have invested your all into this relationship. What are you most likely to recoup by staying with him?

_____

_____

_____

15. Believing your man is all you have means your life is out of balance. Describe how this came to be.

_____

_____

_____

16. Have all your efforts resulted in a more solid bond with him? Explain how.

_____

_____

17. If you readjusted all the compromises and sacrifices you made to keep your man, how different of a person would you be?

_____

_____

_____

18. Do you think he sees you as indispensable because of all you do?

_____

_____

_____

19. Will your clingy ways enhance your self-worth? If putting your all into stopping him from cheating is not enough, what other options are there for you?

_____

_____

_____

20. Because you have given your all in this relationship, you do not have enough energy to leave. Take a realistic assessment of what you will gain if you choose to leave and refocus your energy on yourself.

_____

_____

_____

21. All your efforts have been an act to avoid being abandoned by your man, but in the end, you have abandoned yourself. Were there any true rewards for abandoning yourself?

_____

_____

22. True or false statement; your man became all you had because you made him all you had.

_____

_____

_____

Now, having answered all the questions, what is your truth?

_____

_____

_____

_____

_____

_____

_____

_____

_____

_____

_____

_____

_____

_____

_____

_____

_____

_____

_____

_____

_____

_____

17 I FEEL STUCK

One of the most common reasons for staying I have heard expressed by women in dead-end relationships is the feeling of being stuck. You can relate because you want to leave, but you do not know how or when to leave. Whatever the reason for staying, you will not own your power to exercise your options. When you choose to endure in a less than desirable relationship and have gone against your own value system to stay, you lose the power to make healthy decisions that meet your needs.

You feel stuck because of the long list of barriers you created to challenge any legitimate reasons for leaving. Your power to set and commit to your own boundaries has become weak. Continuing to compromise your values, needs, and desires are the key factors to why you feel stuck. Being stuck is commonly defined as being caught or held in a position, and being unable to move, or being unable to solve a problem. In your case, feeling stuck is a state of mind and not a state of being. In order to reveal your truth, challenge the state of mind you have created. Ask yourself if feeling stuck is more about you or him.

Your sound morals and values have created barriers to leaving in the past. After the first time he cheated, you believed you should stay because of your moral code. You told yourself everyone deserves a second chance, and you worked very hard to forgive and move on. The battle between right and wrong ensued and was the beginning of the mindset that has kept you stuck. This is where you lost your power and sense of justice for your own life. Giving your cheating man a second chance felt like the right thing to do until he cheated again.

To reveal your truth, ask yourself:

1. You have created this feeling of being stuck. What is the fear that keeps you in this dead-end relationship? Do you fear failure, the unknown, or being alone?

   _____

   _____

_____

2. Do you feel guilty about wanting to leave him, feel you don't have the right to leave, or feel you owe him something, and therefore stay?

_____

_____

_____

3. Power comes from knowing your own worth. Has his cheating diminished your sense of worth?

_____

_____

_____

4. What would be the worst-case scenario if you decided to leave?

_____

_____

_____

5. If you were to decide based on what is best for you, what decision would reflect your core values? What decision would feel right for "you"?

_____

_____

_____

6. Based on your morals, you may believe forgiveness is mandatory and everyone deserves a second change. Does what you say and what you think align with what you feel?

_____

_____

_____

7. In what ways have you outgrown this relationship and his cheating?

    _____

    _____

    _____

8. Do you feel stuck because you are not ready to change your lifestyle by doing what it requires for you to live in truth?

    _____

    _____

    _____

9. Do you still feel a secure connection to him? Have you grown cold, distant, and guarded towards him?

    _____

    _____

    _____

10. For all the hurt caused by his cheating, do you believe if you stay he will repay you by being faithful?

    _____

    _____

    _____

11. Are you really stuck, or is your perception about leaving causing you to feel stuck?

    _____

    _____

    _____

12. Leaving will require sacrifices. Are you willing to sacrifice for your own happiness and peace of mind? Could it be you feel stuck because you are not willing to make the sacrifices?

_____

_____

_____

13. Has this relationship satisfied your needs and allowed you to find internal peace?

_____

_____

_____

14. Is getting unstuck an action or a mindset? Do you have to act your way out or think your way out of feeling stuck?

_____

_____

_____

15. Make a list of reasons that reflect why you are choosing to stay. Are you stuck because of what you believe or because of what he has done?

_____

_____

_____

Now, having answered all the questions, what is your truth?

18 I DON'T WANT TO START OVER

What does "I don't want to start over" translate into? Could it mean you don't want to change or make changes? Maybe it means you don't have the energy to invest in someone new. A relationship is a tremendous investment. It is an investment of your time, energy, and dreams. Your heart's desires are invested in the relationship's foundation, and you entered it with the end in mind. You made assessments about whether he was a keeper, if he possessed the potential to become your one-and-only, and if you could see yourself committed to him for the long run. Once you committed to investing your time, energy, and dreams, the thought of starting over became undesirable.

No doubt your evaluation and assessment continued as the two of you dated. You scrutinized his character, habits, and routines to determine if you could envision spending your life with him. By the end of the first few months, you developed a character profile and pondered whether to continue investing in the relationship. The alternative was to consider pulling out and cutting your losses. You stayed, and the rest is history. You don't want to start over, but this choice keeps you stuck with a cheating man. Maybe it's time to do a self-assessment to assist with defining what it means to start over.

To reveal your truth, ask yourself:

1. When you committed to him, you envisioned what your future would entail and how the relationship would make you feel. Has what you envisioned materialized?

    _____

    _____

    _____

2. Have you found it necessary to readjust your needs and vision to account for what you are not getting out of the relationship?

    _____

_____

_____

3. You believed you were in a mutually exclusive, monogamous relationship until you discovered his cheating. What exactly did you think and do once you found out the truth about the betrayal? What decisions did you initially make? Did it require you to start over with a new perspective, vision, and reality about your relationship?

_____

_____

_____

4. After you found out he was cheating, your mind replayed the details of the past. You probably revisited all you did, gave, and sacrificed for the health of the relationship. Did you stay because of him, or because of all you had invested?

_____

_____

_____

5. I know you weighed the pros of staying against the cons of leaving and the cons of staying against the pros of leaving. In your assessment, how much value has the relationship lost because of his cheating and what have you lost?

_____

_____

_____

6. Do you believe you and the relationship will fully recover from the damage caused by his cheating? What beliefs did you revise to make the risk of staying worth the future investment?

_____

_____

7. Did you ever feel you could not continue in the relationship? After you stayed, didn't you have to start over? Did you start over because you felt hope or because you felt stuck?

_____

_____

_____

8. Re-investing in the relationship meant keeping tabs, taking mental notes, and continuously calculating gains and losses. Isn't that exactly what you would have to do in a new relationship with a man with whom you don't have history?

_____

_____

_____

9. Being cheated on zaps you of your energy and damages your self-image. The thought of starting over with someone new is off-putting because you feel you have nothing left to give. Are you staying with your cheating man and putting your heart on lockdown to avoid starting over?

_____

_____

_____

10. You feel that giving of yourself in a new relationship is too risky, but staying with your cheating man carries the same risks. Can you see either way you will have to start over? Describe what starting over would require of you in each scenario.

_____

_____

_____

11. Are you going through the motions in this relationship, or have you truly reinvested yourself?

_____

_____

_____

12. You fear if you leave, you will end up alone or with another cheater. If you stay with an unchanged man, you will still feel lonely and be with a cheater. Which is better; staying with a known cheater or taking a chance on meeting a man who may not be a cheater?

_____

_____

_____

13. Are you projecting your tarnished image of your man onto all men? If you do not want to start over because you fear hooking up with another cheater, how can you find security in staying with a known cheater?

_____

_____

_____

14. You will have to start over if you stay with your cheating man, if you meet another man, and if you choose to be single. Starting over is an automatic occurrence. The choice is yours; how will you choose to start over?

_____

_____

_____

Now, having answered all the questions, what is your truth?

19 HE KNOWS HOW MUCH HE HURT ME SO HE WON'T CHEAT AGAIN

Finding out your man has cheated is crippling news. Trying to find words descriptive enough to make him understand your pain becomes a series of emotional monologues. Your best defense is to put up both physical and emotional walls to shut him out, but the need to make him understand the damage caused by his cheating is overwhelming. This leads you to put the walls down and open up the floodgates, hoping your vulnerability will lead to his fidelity. It becomes your life's mission to make him understand how deeply his cheating has cut.

The problem with getting him to understand your pain is you have to stay wounded in order for him to see how much hurt his cheating has caused. In your wounded state, it will be hard to trust your own judgement. Being wounded will keep you emotional, and staying emotional will lead to using emotional reasoning to make judgement calls. Emotional reasoning and logical thinking cannot exist in the same space. Therefore, your judgement will be impaired by your pain. Your perception of change will be inaccurate, and you will probably mistake his emotional reaction to your pain as readiness to change. Choosing to prolong your pain in the first place is a sign that your judgement is not to be trusted. Who in their right mind chooses to endure pain for longer than necessary and stays in a wounded state to make someone else change? Remaining wounded will keep you stuck with your cheating man in a pitiful world of your own creation.

To reveal your truth, ask yourself:

1. How will you know when your man understands how badly he hurt you, and how will he show signs of caring enough to change?

_____

_____

_____

2. What normally results from seeing someone continuously suffering and in pain is a sense of pity. Do you think pitying you will make him stop cheating? Will being pitiful and wounded be attractive to your man?

    _____

    _____

    _____

3. Do you think your prolonged wounded emotional state will be a burden to him? We normally attempt to relieve ourselves of burdens. Are you risking him wanting to rid himself of you as his burden?

    _____

    _____

    _____

4. Will remaining wounded and having your man feel sorry for you increase your sense of security?

    _____

    _____

    _____

5. Is it your belief an emotional reaction to your hurt and pain will stop him from cheating again? Are you attempting to provoke guilt and shame, hoping it will lead to change?

    _____

    _____

    _____

6. Do you believe knowledge of how harmful something is has the power to change bad habits, character flaws, and inappropriate behaviors?

    _____

_____

_____

7. Go back over the history of your relationship to determine whether you are with a cheater or a man who has cheated. If your assessment shows you are with a cheater, how do you expect your pain to change a cheater?

_____

_____

_____

8. Do you believe it is possible for someone to regret having behaved inappropriately yet still continue that behavior?

_____

_____

_____

9. A cheater's cheating is always about him getting his needs met. His cheating is never about him attending to his woman's needs. Selfishness, not self-sacrifice, drives his cheating. With this being said, has your man showed acts of self-sacrifice over selfishness?

_____

_____

_____

10. How long has he been cheating and lying to you in the process? How many times has he given his all to convince you his lies were the truth?

_____

_____

_____

11. How much time has he spent plotting to enable continuation of his cheating? How often has he been with other women and neglected to assess how you would feel if you were to find out?

_____

_____

_____

12. Has your man seen you hurt in the past while he was actively cheating?

_____

_____

_____

Now, having answered all the questions, what is your truth?

20 MAYBE THIS IS GOD'S WILL
FOR MY LIFE

Why is this happening to me? What did I do to deserve this pain? What is the lesson for me in this? These are typical questions that plague you when your man has cheated. When everyone you have dated from the first boy you labeled your boyfriend to the current one you call your man has cheated, you wonder why. You wonder what you are doing wrong, what you do not have, or what about you is causing men to cheat? The repeated pattern of cheating leads to the belief, if you have done nothing to cause them to cheat, it must be God's will for your life.

Why any woman would believe it is God's will for her to be with a cheater is baffling, but it is a common belief. You begin to believe it must be beyond your control when regardless of all your efforts, changes, and gestures, your man continues to cheat. You are on the right track with this belief because his cheating is beyond your control. However, this thinking goes off-track when you tack on the belief that God has destined you to be with a cheater. When you get biblical, and your rationale leads to a false conclusion, the belief that God is in control of everything starts a chain of thought.

When you can't find an earthly answer for being continuously cheated on, and you can't change another thing about yourself, you make a choice to believe maybe it's God's will for you to be with a cheater. This does not make it easy, but it makes it easier for you to stay with your cheater. It is easier because you get to shift the focus from the real problem, which is your man's cheating, to you being in God's will by staying with your cheater. If you would just take time to look inside yourself, your true beliefs, core values, and morals, then you would have to admit this is a huge stretch of the imagination. What you have done is moralize yourself into staying stuck with a cheater, in the name of God.

To reveal your truth, ask yourself:

1. You decided to forgive him and stayed when he continued to cheat. How does that make it God's will for you to be with a cheater?

_____

_____

_____

2. When the same problems seem to keep recurring no matter what you do, no matter how good you are, and no matter how hard you try to prevent the problem, could the problem be faulty judgment or being a poor judge of character?

_____

_____

_____

3. Is it easier for you to accept that you are destined to be with a cheater or that you have continuously chosen the wrong type of man?

_____

_____

_____

4. You choose to believe it is God's will for you to be with a man who doesn't live in a way that is pleasing to Him. If your man doesn't live in a way that is pleasing to God, why would God destine you to be with him for life?

_____

_____

_____

5. If it's God's will that you spend your life with a cheater, then you don't have a choice in the matter. Could you be using this belief to cushion you from feeling used, weak, or naïve for staying with a cheater? Ponder the different roles of fate and free will. Is it fate, or by your own free will, that you stayed with a cheater?

_____

_____

6. If you believe it's God's will for you to be with a cheater, what will you do when you meet a guy who doesn't cheat? Will you then choose to believe God's will for your life has now changed?

_____

_____

_____

7. Wasn't there a time when you believed you deserved to be in a healthy relationship with a faithful man? Will you continue to settle for less than you once believed you deserved?

_____

_____

_____

8. If God's word states fornication and adultery are both sins, why would it be His will for you to be with a man whose value system allows him to commit both?

_____

_____

_____

9. Did you allow yourself to heal before you enter a new relationship? If not, isn't it likely your wounds, and not God, led you to choose another cheater?

_____

_____

_____

10. The life you are living is the one you created. Do a timeline of all your relationships and connect the dots to develop a clear picture of your role in choosing cheaters, staying with cheaters, and blaming God for being with cheaters. How did your thoughts, actions, immobility, and misbeliefs create this life?

_____

_____

_____

11. If this were God's will for your life, it would not result in you being perpetually defeated, rejected, and disillusioned. There would be growth from the struggle and purpose in the process. Has a greater purpose for your struggle been revealed?

_____

_____

_____

12. Has being with your cheating man diminished your self-worth, dulled your sense of wisdom, or altered your sense of purpose? If you answered yes to any of these questions, it is highly unlikely that it is God's will for you to be with a cheater. Are you ready to admit it has been your will to stay with a cheater and not God's?

_____

_____

_____

13. Have you confused staying with forgiving him? You do not have to stay to forgive, and staying does not mean you have forgiven your man. Have you become bitter, resentful, and/or dissatisfied after staying with him? If so, this is a clear indicator you have not forgiven your man for cheating.

_____

_____

_____

Now, having answered all the questions, what is your truth?

PART 6

"THE SETTLER"

Settling differs from being helpless. While "The Helpless" focuses on what she does not have and will not have, you as "The Settler" copes by sorting through the mess to see what of value remains. Accepting less than what you want, need, or desire somehow gives you a sense of security. You have unsuccessfully tried to implement changes in the relationship and chose not to risk walking away in order to create exactly what you feel you deserve. Instead, you find comfort in adjusting to the cheating by accepting the positively negative life you can have with your cheating man.

Settling for less grows old. Over time, your true wants, needs, and desires will always push up to the surface, becoming harder and harder to ignore. The lies you tell yourself about why you stay with him keep you stuck in a less than desirable relationship. The first lie you told yourself was you knew what you had with him. When he kept proving you did not know what you had with him, you shifted to the lie that being with him is better than being alone. When he kept cheating, you intensified your self-deception by trying to make yourself believe you did not care if he cheated again because he could not hurt you anymore. Acknowledging your truth challenges your ability to continue to settle, but if you continue to ignore your truth, you will continue to be stuck with a cheater.

Revealing your truth will require reprogramming your thinking. It will require you to allow everything you stuffed down and covered up with lies to come to the surface. Take an honest assessment of yourself, not your man, to assist with your ability to reconnect with the true self you abandoned. Acknowledge that you have continuously lied to yourself, just as he has lied to you. Asking yourself the right questions will hold you accountable for the damage that your lies have caused. This will free you from settling and release you to accept only what you want, need, and desire in your life.

21 AT LEAST I KNOW WHAT I HAVE WITH HIM

Just listen to how you talk to yourself. There is no question why you have stayed stuck with your cheating man. You rehearse beliefs like, "It could be worse," "There are a lot of dogs out there," "Every couple has to deal with some drama," and "There are no perfect relationships," just to name a few. These forced beliefs are part of the psychological conditioning created to justify your choice to stay with him. You consider yourself adhering to the perception of seeing the glass as half-full rather than half-empty and being a realist instead of an idealist. This leads to your choice to "hold them" rather than "fold them" when it is obvious he is cheating.

The ultimate belief in knowing what you have with your cheating man is the glue that keeps you stuck, by your own free will. The building blocks of this lie are the constant rationalizing and bargaining that leads you to settle for much less than you truly want and desire. "The Settler" mentality is strengthened by repeatedly allowing his inappropriate behaviors and actions to play out in your relationship. No matter how many new or old boundaries you profess, you are the one who abandons your own values in order to stay with him. You stay after repeated violations of trust and respect, which is more like settling for his cheating than staying because you know what you have with him.

To know what you have with him means you expect him to continue to cheat. Not knowing what you could have with someone new and staying because you know what you have means you have destined yourself to be in a relationship with a cheater. This is the hallmark of settling, because who can really feel secure in a relationship with a known cheater? Your choice to settle has dulled your sense of expectancy, and you somehow take comfort in knowing your man will continue to cheat. Taking some time to get re-acclimated with your true original boundaries and values helps loosen the glue that keeps you stuck with him.

To reveal your truth, ask yourself:

1. What exactly are you acknowledging about your cheating man and professing to know

beyond broken promises, boundary violations, and acts of indiscretion?

_____

_____

_____

2. Make a list of each of his actions that have violated, disregarded, and disrespected your boundaries, values, and needs. Does it feel good to know this is what you will continue to experience?

_____

_____

_____

3. Your original boundaries protected you from disrespect and betrayal? How have you altered your standards in order to stay in this relationship?

_____

_____

_____

4. If you stopped rationalizing and generalizing, and looked at the facts of his cheating, what would it reveal you have with him?

_____

_____

_____

5. There is some good in your man, he is doing some things right, and he honors your relationship in some ways. Make a list of the pros and cons; the good versus the undesirable qualities, what he is doing right versus wrong, and how he honors versus dishonors the relationship.

_____

_____

_____

6. Next, rate the magnitude of the offense beside each entry in direct proportion to how it violates, disregards, and disrespects your core values and boundaries. Do not pay attention to the quantity of entries because that is not of value for this exercise. Use this scale; 1 – no violation, 2 – mild violation, 3 – moderate violation, 4 – serious violation, and 5 – total violation. Add up the score. Do the pros outweigh the cons?

_____

_____

_____

7. You should strive to know yourself better than you know your man. What are your non-negotiable boundaries, even if you have made them negotiable in order to stay with your man?

_____

_____

_____

8. Make a list of your core needs and values. Put a plus sign by those that are being met and a minus sign by those that are being violated. What do you have, a relationship full of pluses or minuses?

_____

_____

_____

9. As you look at your list of pros and cons, and your list of needs and values, are you proud of what you have accepted and allowed? Can you respect your decision to stay with him?

_____

_____

10. Be honest about what needs and values you can allow to be disregarded and those that you cannot compromise. This provides you with an assessment of how you have abandoned, disregarded, and violated yourself and disconnected from your authentic needs, values, and boundaries.

_____

_____

_____

11. Have his actions, behaviors, and character traits taken away from your self-worth, impaired your self-image, or stifled your self-expression? Is the damage reversible?

_____

_____

_____

12. Now that you know what you have with him versus what you need, want, and value, if you choose not to settle, what can you admit to yourself? Who do you have to be in order to stay with him? What would happen if you reconnected to each part of you that was abandoned in order to stay with him?

_____

_____

_____

13. Does it benefit you more to know what you have with him or to know that you are firmly connected to your true self? Can you do both simultaneously?

_____

_____

_____

Now, having answered all the questions, what is your truth?

_____

_____

_____

_____

_____

_____

_____

_____

_____

_____

_____

_____

_____

_____

_____

_____

_____

_____

_____

_____

22 BEING WITH MY CHEATING MAN IS BETTER THAN BEING ALONE

If anyone asked you about your relationship preference, you would not hesitate to let them know you are a one-man woman. You prefer committed relationships to the dating scene. Maybe you were conditioned to be this way by the elder women in your family. It's possible that movies and television shows have strengthened your predisposition to preferring the label girlfriend over single. Listening to love songs on the radio that sing about love, commitment, and fidelity could also sway your preference. Even if you are the only one committed to the relationship, you will remain steadfast and immovable because your preference is not to be alone. Therefore, you have grown to accept that being with a cheating man is better.

Being single and being incomplete became synonymous. You paid a high price to avoid being alone by settling for men who did not fit the profile of the partner you envisioned. You paid with your self-respect and self-worth because it is hard to respect yourself and feel worthy when you choose to stay with a cheating man. You also paid with your self-regard because you constantly disregard your own values when you accept that your man is cheating. The price you paid to avoid being alone far exceeds the hurt which would eventually heal after you let go of what was causing the pain. Avoiding being alone has kept you stuck with a cheating man.

To reveal your truth, ask yourself:

1. If you believe being with a cheating man is better than being alone, you have become quite creative. Could you use that same creativity to believe that being alone is better than being with a cheating man?

_____

_____

_____

2. In order to challenge faulty thinking, you will have to create *The Middle*. Do this by creating a timeline of the actual relationship history with your cheating man. List all the details of his affairs, how you felt, how he treated you, and what you sacrificed.

_____

_____

_____

3. Next, evaluate the reality of how life has actually been with him. Use the list from Number 2 to honestly evaluate if it is better to be with your cheating man than to be alone.

_____

_____

_____

4. Create another timeline in six-month increments, but this time fill in *The Middle* of each time frame with a detailed list of what you lost, what you gained, and what you settled for while trying to avoid being alone. Was it really better to have stayed with your cheating man than to have been alone?

_____

_____

_____

5. How do you believe others perceive the two of you as a couple? How do you think you would be perceived as a single woman who has left a cheating man?

_____

_____

_____

6. Does being with a cheating man cause you to feel alone and lonely? How often were you alone while staying with him?

_____

_____

_____

7. Now that you have done your timelines, how do you envision your life would have been if you left instead of staying?

_____

_____

_____

8. It is important to be truthful about who you are and acknowledge your non-negotiables. The ability to accept your man is cheating, without it causing your self-worth to diminish, is "do-able" for some women. Are you one of those women, or is cheating on your non-negotiable list of behaviors?

_____

_____

_____

9. Can you trust him? Do you need trust and fidelity to feel secure in your relationship? Do you feel secure with him now?

_____

_____

_____

10. Do you feel stressed, depressed, or anxious because of staying with him? If not, it is better to be with your cheating man than to be alone? If you feel depressed or anxious, then it is not better for you to be with your cheating man than to be alone.

_____

_____

_____

11. Are you forcing yourself to accept something you find morally unacceptable?

_____

_____

_____

12. Does being with a cheating man make you clingy, paranoid, and/or crazy? Does it complement (add to your worth/complete) you or diminish (reduce your worth/restrict) you?

_____

_____

_____

13. Are you staying with him because you are afraid of being alone or afraid of what you fear you won't be able to have?

_____

_____

_____

14. Does being single mean you will be lonely? Is it possible to be single and not lonely as well as possible to be with a cheating man and lonely?

_____

_____

_____

Now, having answered all the questions, what is your truth?

_____

_____

_____

_____

_____

_____

_____

_____

_____

_____

_____

_____

_____

_____

_____

_____

_____

_____

_____

23 I DON'T CARE ANYMORE
SO HIS CHEATING CAN'T HURT ME

Nothing is more disheartening than taking a chance on your man changing and cleaning up his act, only to discover he is cheating again. Repeated exposure to his cheating has caused you to resort to the defense mechanism of emotional numbing, which helps you believe the lie you don't care if he cheats again. As the numbing intensifies, you convince yourself his cheating cannot hurt you anymore. This nonchalant attitude allows you to maintain your current relationship with him without acknowledging you are settling for behaviors you vowed to never accept.

"I don't care" is the equivalent of erecting an emotional wall around your heart. It is a form of emotional anesthesia for the pain caused by the betrayal. When you lie to yourself and attempt to believe you don't care if he continues to cheat, this mentality dulls the pain, but it does not heal the wound. It is like medical anesthesia administered before a procedure. You do not feel a thing as long as the anesthesia is active, but at some point the effects of the anesthesia wear off, leaving you exposed to the pain. Eventually, your ability to maintain your emotional numbness will wear off. Then you will have to deal with the feelings you have become so good at numbing.

Repeatedly telling yourself you do not care if he cheats again helps you master the art of dealing with his cheating in a methodical and practical manner. This gives you a false sense of control. Of course, your true preference is to feel secure in the relationship with the man you call yours. In order to reveal your truth, find the courage to tear down the emotional walls and admit that you care about him cheating again. Stop settling for the comfort in the discomfort and the false sense of security in the lie that he cannot hurt you anymore. Dealing with your truth will be the only means of getting unstuck.

To reveal your truth, ask yourself:

1. Knowing your man will cheat again and having to deny you care will never result in security. If you have to stay emotionally disconnected from him in order to stay, what

kind of relationship will you have?

_____

_____

_____

2. Love grows from security, trust, and mutual respect. Exactly what is growing in this relationship?

_____

_____

_____

3. You are minimizing your discomfort with his cheating by putting up emotional walls and trying not to care that he cheats. If you do not care if he cheats, what exactly do you care about?

_____

_____

_____

4. Being emotionally numb will only lead to feeling spiritually and emotionally dead. If your dreams, happiness, and faith in fidelity are all numbed, what will sustain the relationship? What will the foundation of your relationship be if you continue to be emotionally numb?

_____

_____

_____

5. What are you allowing to happen to yourself while you allow your man to continue to cheat?

_____

_____

_____

6. If you do not hurt when he cheats, what do you feel? What will happen to you if you continue to feel this way? Are you opting for a long-term relationship of misery by staying with him?

_____

_____

_____

7. Is staying with him altering your entire belief system regarding the dynamics of a healthy, intimate relationship? Are you eliminating the possibility of having a relationship with a man who does not cheat?

_____

_____

_____

8. You are lying to yourself about not caring if he cheats again. Are you maintaining this lie because it is easier to say you do not care than admit you have wasted your time, energy, tears, and youth on a man who will never be who you want him to be? What are you really protecting by staying, and what will leaving cost?

_____

_____

_____

9. Do you cringe when you hear love stories or doubt the authenticity of other's commitment? Have you become cynical?

_____

_____

_____

10. Has staying with your cheating man and not caring disabled your ability to expect and receive love? Has the bitterness and resentment that lead to you becoming emotionally numb limited your access to real love?

_____

_____

_____

11. Because you do not care, you say he cannot hurt you anymore with his cheating. Are you hurting yourself if you do not allow yourself to care? In what ways are you hurting yourself if you continue to stay with a cheater?

_____

_____

_____

12. Could your emotional walls be creating a coffin rather than a protective barrier for your feelings? Do you realize you cannot get back the years spent in numbness?

_____

_____

_____

13. After years of not caring and being emotionally numb, what will it take for you to reconnect with your core beliefs and values, to accept the truth, and to love yourself? How will this affect your ability to feel genuine emotions with another man if you leave?

_____

_____

_____

14. Are you willing to accept the fact that the person who is cheating on you is actually "you?" Are you able to accept that the person who you stopped caring about is "you?"

_____

_____

_____

15. Are you willing to admit by not caring if he cheats again you have stopped caring about your values, needs, and security?

_____

_____

_____

Now, having answered all the questions, what is your truth?

_____

_____

_____

_____

_____

_____

_____

_____

_____

_____

_____

_____

_____

_____

_____

_____

_____

_____

_____

_____

_____

_____

_____

_____

PART 7

"THE SAVIOR"

So, you want to be "The Savior" of your failing relationship? Saving the relationship is a tall order to fill on your own. Because you are with a cheater, you will be responsible for fixing what he broke. Then, you have to redeem him from the cheating ways that destroyed the relationship. Once that is complete, you can restore the relationship and revive what has died. That is what a savior does, but you are not a savior.

The Savior mentality burdens you with all the work. I bet you have an "S" on your chest prepared to conquer the impossible by saving the relationship and transform it into a loving, monogamous union. Sadly, you have not mastered the skill of recognizing when you are facing an impossible mission. Forgiveness is the key factor in saving your relationship, and as a woman of faith you strongly adhere to the creed of forgiving those who trespass against you. The commitment to forgive has led you to miscalculate the most realistic outcome. You mistake forgiving with staying and believe choosing to leave is an act of unforgiveness. This perception keeps you stuck with your cheating man.

If you have established a family with him, your traditional values will keep you stuck. You not only have the mission of saving the marriage, you also have the arduous task of saving the family. Even though you have no earthly idea how you will trust him again, you vow to stay for the sake of the family. You mistake staying with saving the family.

As savior of the relationship, a second chance means you have time to intervene. You set a plate in front of him, seasoned with the ingredients for a faithful man because his plate is empty. Your hope is as long as you keep feeding him, he will grow strong in his ability to change his cheating ways. A second chance turns into another and another. If you would abandon the lie, you would realize the truth the only one you can save is you.

24 I WANT TO SAVE MY RELATIONSHIP

Women more often than men see the potential for "forever" even when a relationship is showing signs of distress. You are one of these women and have put an "S" on your chest assuming the superhero role to save your distressed relationship. Even though your man shows no motivation to change, and sometimes acts in ways that sabotage your efforts, you continue on with your mission. It will take a miracle to save your relationship when your man is not actively engaged in the process. The lies you have told yourself have kept you stuck with your cheating man.

You are the type of woman who does whatever it takes to save what is of value. If the long-term effects of your efforts are positive, then you reap a worthy benefit. However, if your hard work does not pay off, you could easily turn into a martyr who continuously dies to self in order to sacrifice for the relationship. A savior dies to self and acts sacrificially for the greater good. If no good is developing out of your sacrificial acts, then what exactly are you saving? Chew on this concept and free yourself from the lie you can save a relationship that has died many deaths.

To reveal your truth, ask yourself:

1. Start by clearly defining the relationship you have with your cheating man. Next, clearly define the problems with no filters.

   _____

   _____

   _____

2. What does the word "save" mean to you when acting to save your relationship?

   _____

   _____

   _____

3. What will saving the relationship require of and from you? What will saving the relationship cause you to feel about yourself?

_____

_____

_____

4. It is possible but less common to hear of a rescue, salvage, or revival being accomplished single handedly. Is he motivated and actively assisting with the mission to save the relationship?

_____

_____

_____

5. Be honest about what you really have in the relationship. Are you striving to save the potential that you believe the relationship has or the relationship that you actually have? Is the relationship desirable "as is?"

_____

_____

_____

6. Is your mission to save the relationship driven by the fear of being alone?

_____

_____

_____

7. Is your effort to save the relationship motivated by trying to avoid failure or feeling like a failure? Are you trying to avoid being ridiculed by others? Is the end of a relationship always considered a failure?

_____

_____

_____

8. Are you trying to save the relationship because it is what women in your family do?

    _____

    _____

    _____

9. Are you attempting to save the relationship to avoid the pain that follows a breakup?

    _____

    _____

    _____

10. The only relationship you can save is the relationship with yourself. Are you setting clear, appropriate relationship boundaries that assist with respecting yourself?

    _____

    _____

    _____

11. You profess to love your cheating man and therefore want to save the relationship. Unless you show self-love, you cannot possibly have a healthy relationship with a man. How are you showing self-love in this relationship? How is staying with your cheating man showing self-love?

    _____

    _____

    _____

12. Is your motivation to save your relationship driven by insecurity and an unhealthy attachment to your cheating man? Is the need to be in control the motivating factor for saving the relationship?

_____

_____

_____

13. Will saving the relationship include setting boundaries that will cause him to treat you with respect and high regard? What is your respect level for yourself, and how do you show self-respect?

_____

_____

_____

14. Have you lost yourself in your man? Have you sacrificed your values, desires, and goals to keep him? Do you need to save yourself or him?

_____

_____

_____

15. Are you trying to save the relationship because you feel you have compromised and sacrificed too much to allow it to end? Are you attempting to save your investment in the relationship or your relationship with your cheating man?

_____

_____

_____

16. Do you avoid certain actions and comments out of fear of making him cheat again? Do you feel you will push him away if you do not act a certain way or do certain things? Do you think you can stop him from cheating again?

_____

_____

_____

17. Do you have conversations with yourself and others about how much you have put up with and given up to be with your cheating man? If so, you are attempting to save your investment. Which is worth saving, the relationship or your investment into the relationship?

_____

_____

_____

18. Is your mood frequently anxious, depressed, or sad? Do you experience a sense of emptiness or restlessness in this relationship?

_____

_____

_____

19. How has your relationship with yourself evolved while continuing to stay with your cheating man? How much have you departed from your core values and altered your belief system in order to save the relationship?

_____

_____

_____

20. Is it safe to say you do not want the relationship you now have? What you actually want is for the relationship to change into what you truly desire. Do you desire a relationship that will allow you to be true to self, foster self-respect, and provide a sense of security? Can you have this in your current relationship?

_____

_____

_____

Now, having answered all the questions, what is your truth?

_____

_____

_____

_____

_____

_____

_____

_____

_____

_____

_____

_____

_____

_____

_____

_____

_____

_____

_____

_____

_____

_____

25 I'M A CHRISTIAN SO
I HAVE TO FORGIVE HIM

It has benefited you to live by traditional Christian principles. Principles like, "Forgive those who trespass against you," "Forgive and you shall be forgiven," and "Forgive your enemies," make up the moral code you aspire to honor. Therefore, you do not depart from your code of conduct when your man has cheated. You are still human, so when you find out he cheated you go ballistic, lose your religion, and curse the day that you ever met this lying cheater. However, after some time you regroup, and you vow to forgive.

Is your forgiveness a means of bargaining with God to bless you with a repentant and reformed man who will no longer cheat? If so, this will lead you to miscalculate outcomes and remain stuck with him in the name of religion. You believe to forgive is to stay with him, and to leave is to not forgive him for his transgressions. You underestimate the extent of the work required to heal the hurt and move past the betrayal. You mistakenly believe your forgiveness will take care of it all.

A spirit of resentment will surface because of the extent of the unattended wounds you are attempting to heal with forgiveness. You won't see it coming, but it will emerge in full force. This will trigger a self-righteous Christian demeanor that will cause you to attempt to control his actions. If you can actually forgive from your heart, you could get unstuck and release your man from your wrath. Forgiving because you have to as a Christian will leave you stuck with a cheater, and the truth is you are mad as hell. The Savior mentality and the true Christian character are not the same.

To reveal your truth, ask yourself:

1. Have you attempted to create shame and guilt in him? Are you seeking to make him feel the same hurt and pain his cheating caused you?

    _____

    _____

2. Are you beating him down with scriptures that magnify his sinful nature to ensure he will not cheat again? How do judgment and forgiveness work together?

_____

_____

_____

3. Do you consider staying with your man a condition and demonstration of forgiveness? Does staying mean that you have forgiven?

_____

_____

_____

4. Are you experiencing bitterness and resentment? Have you released him from his debt to you?

_____

_____

_____

5. Do you feel he owes you for staying and should repay you by repenting?

_____

_____

_____

6. Are you attempting to control his urges to cheat with your actions of judging, preaching, and moralizing?

_____

_____

_____

7. Are you sentencing your cheater to reside in your prison, in the name of forgiveness, to save the relationship?

_____

_____

_____

8. Did you experience a sense of freedom from bondage when you forgave him, or did you experience a need to monitor and control his thoughts and behaviors?

_____

_____

_____

9. Do you see the parallel in his choice to cheat and your choice to forgive? Do you see how his choice to cheat was all about him and had nothing to do with you? Do you see how your choice to forgive should be all about you and have nothing to do with what he does to deserve forgiveness?

_____

_____

_____

10. Are you trying to act like you have forgiven him, or have you truly forgiven? Has your forgiveness become a behavioral contract or a process of release? Have you put your halo on to shine a light on his transgressions?

_____

_____

_____

11. Are you making it your business to monitor every little step he takes? Do you believe it is your duty to save him from his cheating ways?

_____

_____

_____

12. Do you believe forgiveness is going to change him? Are you considering his history of cheating, his character, and his value system?

_____

_____

_____

13. Are you bargaining with God and expecting Him to change your man's cheating ways as a reward for your willingness to forgive?

_____

_____

_____

14. Do you need him to act, look, and be a certain way in order for you to forgive?

_____

_____

_____

15. Are you expecting forgiveness to automatically heal your wounds? Are you acknowledging your hurt, or do you believe prolonged feelings of hurt equate to unforgiveness?

_____

_____

_____

Now, having answered all the questions, what is your truth?

_____

_____

_____

_____

_____

_____

_____

_____

_____

_____

_____

_____

_____

_____

_____

_____

_____

_____

_____

_____

_____

_____

_____

26 I DON'T WANT TO
BREAK UP MY FAMILY

Your favorite sitcom depicts the life of a perfect family, complete with a mom, a dad, and well-balanced children. Being raised in a two-parent home probably conditioned you to believe this is best for your child as well. If you grew up in a single-parent home, you probably longed for the fairytale of a two-parent home. Giving your child the structure and balance of living in a two-parent home is traditionally a standard of success. Keeping the family together, no matter how healthy or dysfunctional, unfortunately is a very common goal. What is best for the family becomes the focal point of most decisions.

"The Savior" mindset puts you in the position to endure pain and struggling. Doing all, sacrificing all, and being all for the family while neglecting your own needs will eventually lead you to lose sight of your own boundaries. No matter how many times he misses the mark, his cheating will be overlooked, dismissed, and minimized. Your dream of having the perfect family life with your child and your man anchors you in the relationship, and this will keep you stuck with your cheating man.

His choices are destroying the health and security of the family, and you are struggling to keep the family together. In order to save anything, there has to be a way to stop the process or end an action, to keep something safe. If he is choosing to cheat, you do not possess the power to stop him, to end his action, or to keep your relationship safe. There is no way for you to break up the family when your man is the one cheating. The only thing you can do is decide whether you will stay or go. The moment he cheated, the family was broken.

To reveal your truth, ask yourself:

1. What exactly are you trying to save? Are you trying to save your dream of what the family could be or what you currently have with your cheating man?

_____

_____

_____

2. Does your man share your values? Does he think the family is worth sacrificing his wants? Is he an active part of your child's life without you structuring the time they spend together?

_____

_____

_____

3. Have you and your man mapped out your life together? Have you started your own family traditions, do you share family responsibilities, and are you equally committed to fidelity?

_____

_____

_____

4. Your vision for the perfect family was interrupted when he cheated. Do you acknowledge the real threat to the security of your family is him?

_____

_____

_____

5. Is it possible to have a strong healthy family if your relationship with him is weak? What has his betrayal done to the two of you as a couple?

_____

_____

_____

6. What did he say or do that made you think he would change? What influenced you to think you can prevent the breakup of the family?

_____

_____

_____

7. What needs and wants did you have to abandon to stay with him?

_____

_____

_____

8. Was cheating one of your deal-breakers? How did you live with the thing you vowed to never accept? What did you have to alter to make it work?

_____

_____

_____

9. Are you trying to save the family because you do not want to be alone, raise a child alone, or be a statistic? Are you attempting to avoid the stigma of being a single mother?

_____

_____

_____

10. Did your gut tell you to leave him before you got pregnant? Because you didn't listen, do you feel guilty and responsible for saving the family?

_____

_____

_____

11. Are you protecting the script you created in your head about the family you dream of having, or are you trying to save the family as it exists today?

_____

_____

_____

12. Why are you taking responsibility for saving the family when it was your man's cheating that caused the damage?

_____

_____

_____

13. Would your choice to leave him really break up the family or was it caused by his cheating?

_____

_____

_____

14. What was he doing to the family in all the hours, days, weeks, and months he repeatedly cheated?

_____

_____

_____

15. Did you and your man establish a solid foundation to survive his repeated cheating? Is your connection solid enough for you to survive this betrayal?

_____

_____

_____

16. Do you believe your family bond will strengthen after each affair?

_____

_____

17. Are you a woman who can truly forgive your man for cheating? Can you stay with him after he has cheated without being haunted by the thoughts of his affair?

_____

_____

_____

18. Saving the family has to be the right thing for you and has to benefit you. Can you describe how it benefits you to save the family?

_____

_____

_____

19. If saving the family is for the child, and the parents are not in a healthy relationship, what are you actually saving? Will the child witness warmth, compassion, trust, and honesty if you stay?

_____

_____

_____

20. If keeping the child in a home with parents that display love is saving the family, what is keeping the child in a home where the parents are disconnected doing?

_____

_____

_____

21. Have you and your man been able to establish healthy communication, effective conflict resolution, and mutual respect since he was caught cheating?

_____

_____

_____

22. Are you aiding in the breakup and disconnect of the family by trying to fix a relationship that is seriously fragmented? Will staying in a fragmented family save it?

_____

_____

_____

23. Re-write your script and re-think the meaning of family. Re-think what really makes you, your man, and your child a family. Can you be a family even if you two are not a couple?

_____

_____

_____

Now, having answered all the questions, what is your truth?

_____

_____

_____

_____

_____

_____

_____

_____

_____

_____

_____

_____

_____

_____

_____

_____

_____

_____

_____

_____

_____

_____

27 I HAVE TO GIVE HIM
A CHANCE TO CHANGE

Let's set the record straight; you are not a weak woman who cannot maintain boundaries. You are not dumb or stupid, but your actions might lead men to experience you as naïve because you are a woman of principle who has standards. You are simply abiding by a traditional moral code of ethics, which leads you to believe that everybody deserves a chance to change. Your naivety is in determining how many chances to allow.

The path to a "chance to change" is long and bumpy. It starts off as a self-righteous gesture where you decide to grace your cheating man with a chance to change into the person who you thought he was. Conflict arises when you realize he is not who you thought he was and will never be the man you want him to be. In that moment of clarity, instead of accepting the truth, you decide to try harder to change him and insist he also tries harder. Inner conflict intensifies when you abandon parts of yourself and your desires in order to give your cheating man a chance to change. Here is where you get stuck and could remain stuck unless you will accept the truth. Getting unstuck could be as simple as taking the time to look back, connect the dots, and identify truthfully if there has been any lasting change.

To reveal your truth, ask yourself:

1. List five conditions that are most important for a successful relationship. How many of the things listed do you have with your man?

   _____

   _____

   _____

2. What do you tell yourself you don't understand about your man? Look deeper and determine if you don't understand or you see something you do not want to accept.

   _____

_____

_____

3. How has he justified his cheating? What explanations has he given for his actions? What would have to be different for you to believe he has changed? While in the process of giving him a chance to change, have you witnessed anything that you have identified as important to the success of the relationship?

_____

_____

_____

4. How do you see this change happening? For example, shame and guilt leading to change, resentment and regret leading to change, or spiritual awakening leading to change? Who has the blueprint for his change, you or him?

_____

_____

_____

5. Has he continued to profess his love for you and his remorse for cheating? Do you think this is what will lead to change?

_____

_____

_____

6. Has your choice to give him a chance to change come from seeing signs of change or from him telling you of the changes he plans to make? Is he able to identify your needs and what he did wrong without your input?

_____

_____

_____

7. Have you given him a list of do's and don'ts to help him change? Will this list lead to the change you seek? If you feel you have to give him a list to assist with his change, will it result in genuine change or the ability to follow instructions? Are you expecting him to change or to abide by your instructions and demands?

    _____

    _____

    _____

8. What do you think would happen if you didn't give him the list of do's and don'ts? Are you making yourself responsible for his change or are you allowing him to show you he has changed?

    _____

    _____

    _____

9. Think about his morals and values, decision-making skills, actions, and behaviors. What have you witnessed him changing on his own without your input?

    _____

    _____

    _____

10. What has time shown? Do you care about what he is motivated to change on his own, or are you more concerned about his ability to abide by your list of demands and commands?

    _____

    _____

    _____

11. Are you giving him a chance to change or a chance to perform? If you are giving him a chance to change, you are allowing time to show you who he is. If you have given him a

script filled with cues, directions, and corrections, you are giving him a chance to perform.

_____

_____

_____

12. Can you trust him to change? Are you able to feel secure in your choice to give him a chance to change?

_____

_____

_____

Now, having answered all the questions, what is your truth?

_____

_____

_____

_____

_____

_____

_____

_____

_____

_____

_____

_____

_____

_____

_____

_____

_____

_____

_____

_____

_____

_____

_____

_____

PART 8

"THE COMPROMISER"

Your coping style as "The Compromiser" is quite interesting. You are a little blind, a bit of a dreamer, and a settler all rolled up into a practical way of thinking that renders you stuck with your cheating man. Your blindness makes it possible for you to only see what you want to see. The dreamer in you sees the potential for minimal harm instead of the reality of ongoing betrayal. The settler in you believes if you give up some of what you really want, in the end you will gain some of what you need. Put it all together and you have graduated to thinking and acting as "The Compromiser."

Your way of blending the idea of the perfect relationship in your head with the flaws of your true relationship keeps your hope alive. You compromise your way into believing your man has qualities that are not truly there. You rationalize the flaws to convince yourself that what you are putting up with will payoff in the end. These lies, along with the way you twist and bend your values to fit his flaws, keep you stuck compromising with his cheating. When your logical way of thinking bargains with your emotions, and your head bargains with your heart, it results in a compromised version of the truth. The give-and-take, the pros and cons, and weighing the costs against the benefits all give way to the ultimate compromise. Getting unstuck will require you to take time to deal with only the facts and reality of your current relationship. The facts will shed light on reality and reality will open your mind to the truth.

28 HE TAKES CARE OF ME

Why would you logically stay with a cheating man, and what could you possibly gain? You have mastered the art of creating an uncomfortable-comfort, a negative-positive, and a lose-win relationship with your man. The foundation of your belief is, "he takes care of me." Who doesn't want to be taken care of?

The problem here is he is not actually taking care of you. To take care of something you have to know what it needs to be its best and watch how it responds to what you do. You have to pay attention, be in tune with, and be willing to make adjustments as needed to provide the best care. To take care of something, you have to recognize the signs that what you are doing is not working and when there is a positive response to what you are doing. Your man is missing the mark in all these areas, so how can you continue to believe he takes care of you?

Your ability to rationalize and bargain with your beliefs has led to the misbelief that he is taking care of you. You built an arsenal of lies around the thought that you stay with him because he takes care of you. This misconception keeps you stuck with a cheater who has acted in ways that have proven him only capable of taking care of his own wants and needs. He wants you to represent to the world you two share that he is a good man. For this reason, he provides things that will show the image of himself he holds. He provides for you, and this differs from him taking care of you. Peel back the layers of the lies you wrapped around the truth to get unstuck.

To reveal your truth, ask yourself:

1. What does it mean to be taken care of?

   _____

   _____

   _____

2. Write everything you believe he does to take care of you. Is he taking care of you or providing you with things? Are you being provided for or taken care of?

_____

_____

_____

3. If you replaced the art of rationalization with the science of observation, what would you see? What facts would you see as proof that he is taking care of you and not providing for you?

_____

_____

_____

4. Being provided for means there is tangible evidence of your man's presence in your life, i.e. he gives you nice things. Has he ever said it's important for him to provide for you? Is being a good provider a part of his image?

_____

_____

_____

5. Do you see him as a responsible individual who makes sure things are taken care of? Are you confusing his efforts to take care of things with him taking care of you?

_____

_____

_____

6. In order to take care of someone, you need to know what it takes for them to thrive and to be their best. Is your man connected to you in a way that he can sense what you need to thrive and for you to be your best? How does his cheating factor into this equation?

_____

_____

7. In order to take care of someone, you have to know the dos and don'ts that apply to their values. You also have to watch how they respond to what you do. Your boundaries are your dos and don'ts of how to properly care for you. Is he honoring and respecting your boundaries? Is he paying attention to how you respond to his cheating?

_____

_____

_____

8. Taking care of someone means you are paying attention to their needs, in-tune with how your actions make them feel, and willing to make the necessary adjustments. Is this how your man functions in your relationship? Has he paid attention to your needs and how his cheating has hurt you? Has he stopped cheating to take care of you? Is he in tune with your feelings and making the necessary behavioral adjustments to never hurt you in that way again?

_____

_____

_____

9. Are you using the things your man does for you as a trade-off for the hurt his cheating has caused?

_____

_____

_____

10. Do you constantly work to list the things he does or provides in order to feel justified in staying with a cheater?

_____

_____

_____

11. Is it possible for him to take care of you and continue to cheat at the same time? Is it possible for him to continue to violate your trust and take care of you at the same time?

_____

_____

_____

12. Is it possible for him to be in-tune with and connected to you but continue to cheat?

_____

_____

_____

13. What effect has his cheating had on you, the relationship, and your sense of worth?

_____

_____

_____

14. Does what matters to you matter to him? Does it matter to you that he does not honor your values and has not set the appropriate boundaries to protect your relationship?

_____

_____

_____

15. How are you taking care of yourself in this relationship with a cheater? Are you honoring your values, needs, wants, and boundaries? Do you feel emotionally stable when he cheats? Are you taking care of yourself by staying with a man who continues to cheat?

_____

_____

_____

Now, having answered all the questions, what is your truth?

_____

_____

_____

_____

_____

_____

_____

_____

_____

_____

_____

_____

_____

_____

_____

_____

_____

_____

_____

_____

_____

_____

_____

_____

_____

29 EVERYBODY HAS TO DEAL WITH SOMETHING IN THEIR RELATIONSHIP

There are no perfect people, so there are no perfect relationships. Although there are no perfect people, there is a person who is perfect for you. Your values and needs should be reflected in who you choose for your partner. Most women look for qualities that are unique to their needs when entering a relationship. However, what we all need is to feel appreciated, respected, and valued. Cheating creates the opposite of this in a relationship.

Your past relationship history left scars, heartaches, and regrets that developed into your current needs. The cheating in your failed relationships has morphed into needs you seek to fulfill in your current situation. These needs governed what you said you would and would not tolerate until constant compromising weakened your boundaries. When you are busy trying to get your needs met, you enter a zone that blinds you and distorts your perception of the truth. When the same inappropriate behavior continues to recur with different partners, fear begins to make decisions for you. Fear leads to boundaries that are too weak and flexible, and this is how "The Compromiser" is born. Before long, you live by a different motto; "Everybody Has to Deal with Something." Now you are stuck putting up with behaviors that you swore never to allow in your relationship.

To get unstuck, you will have to open your eyes to see what is really there. Challenge the give-and-take mentality, and revisit your core values. It will require you to determine whether the "something" you are dealing with is something you can honestly live with. Be willing to uncompromisingly assess if the "something" you are dealing with is really dealing with you.

To reveal your truth, ask yourself:

1. You have already made a list of pros and cons to assist with validating your decision to stay with your cheating man. Clarify for yourself exactly what makes a con a con and a pro a pro. What need is being compromised when you accept each con?

_____

_____

2. Are you comparing the inappropriate behavior of this partner to that of past partners and creating a false measure of acceptable behavior? Are you able to view this relationship in isolation instead of in comparison to what your friends and family are dealing with?

_____

_____

_____

3. Exactly what measure are you using to determine what you will tolerate? Why have you put up with his cheating?

_____

_____

_____

4. Do you feel comfortable, secure, and validated in this relationship?

_____

_____

_____

5. A big part of your willingness to accept the belief that everybody has to deal with something is because of self-betrayal. How have you betrayed your own value system, forfeited being respected, and accepted unacceptable behavior by staying with him?

_____

_____

_____

6. Has dealing with his cheating started to deal with you by diminishing your level of well-being, self-respect, and self-confidence?

_____

_____

_____

7. What happens to you emotionally when you continuously re-write the script to fit the circumstances you find yourself in rather than rely on your true values as your guide?

_____

_____

_____

8. What will happen when you exhaust all possibilities of forcing this relationship into a version of a reality that you feel you can deal with?

_____

_____

_____

9. Review your list of pros and cons to determine if the good outweighs the bad. Are you using your feelings, your values, your morals, and your needs to measure the pros and the cons to identify what is good or bad for you?

_____

_____

_____

10. Are you properly measuring the weight of each offense? What measure of weight have you given his cheating? Be sure not to assign improper weight to a behavior that you consider non-negotiable, goes against your value system, and makes you redefine your worth.

_____

_____

11. Are you a woman who can deal with your man's cheating without it diminishing your sense of well-being? Can you deal with his cheating and maintain a healthy self-image and a healthy sense of worth?

_____

_____

_____

12. Do you find that you have to minimize the significance and impact of his cheating on your well-being in order to stay?

_____

_____

_____

13. Are you being totally honest with yourself about the non-negotiable nature of cheating as it relates to your core values, or are you creating a self-deceptive means of viewing his cheating in order to compromise your way into dealing with the cheating?

_____

_____

_____

14. Does it become harder and harder to deal with his cheating over time? What part of you has to die in order for you to deal with his cheating? What part of the relationship has died because of his cheating?

_____

_____

_____

15. Are you trying to pass off something you consider unacceptable as something you can accept? Is there a nagging sense of discomfort or discontentment that keeps you longing to have your true needs met?

_____

_____

_____

16. Has your need to be in a healthy, monogamous, mutually exclusive relationship faded away? Can you deal with his cheating and stay true to your values at the same time?

_____

_____

_____

17. Have you been able to heal from the wounds caused by his cheating? Are you accepting his cheating as a trade-off for accepting the belief that everybody has to deal with something in their relationship?

_____

_____

_____

18. How do you react and feel when he lies to you? How do you react and feel when you lie to yourself?

_____

_____

_____

19. Are your core needs being met? Have you reduced your core needs to insignificant wants to justify staying?

_____

---

20. Do you realize self-deception is far more dangerous than any lie he has told you? Do you realize with each betrayal you have to deceive yourself in order to deal with his cheating?

Now, having answered all the questions, what is your truth?

_____

_____

_____

_____

_____

_____

_____

_____

_____

_____

_____

_____

_____

_____

_____

_____

_____

_____

_____

_____

30 AS LONG AS HE'S RESPECTFUL WITH HIS CHEATING I DON'T CARE

When your man has cheated repeatedly, it can create a sense of becoming desensitized to the pain, disrespect, and betrayal. You begin to categorize the cheating in a way that makes one indiscretion better than another or one betrayal more acceptable than another. To assist with coping, you create the foolishness of the good versus bad cheating, the right versus the wrong way to cheat, and the respectful versus the disrespectful way to cheat. The lie that *as long as he's respectful with his cheating I don't care* helps you cope with the repeated indiscretions, but is it possible for respect and cheating to exist at the same time?

You care that he cheats and feel his cheating is disrespectful. It does matter that he continues to hurt, violate, and disrespect you. The lie that you don't care continues to exist because of your need to believe it is possible for cheating to be respectful. The effects of embracing this lie have led to the continuous compromising of everything that makes sense to you. Reconnecting with your true beliefs, values, and emotions will help to release you from compromising all that you believe. It will also lead you to release the lies you have used to create the illusion of a healthy relationship with your cheating man.

To reveal your truth, ask yourself:

1. Based on your true core values, is it possible for cheating to be considered respectful? Is it possible for him to respect you and cheat at the same time?

   _____

   _____

   _____

2. Is he being respectful of your feelings, emotions, time, wants, and needs when he cheats? Is he being respectful of your values, boundaries, dreams and future when he cheats? Exactly what is he being respectful of when he cheats?

_____

_____

_____

3. Is it possible to keep his cheating in the streets and between him and the other woman? Has he ever texted or called his woman while you were with him?

_____

_____

_____

4. Does the fact that nobody but you, him, and the other woman knows about his cheating make it respectful? Do you pretend not to know as much as you actually know, to consider his cheating respectful?

_____

_____

_____

5. The word "cheating" is synonymous with tricking, deceiving, dishonoring, defrauding, scamming, and duping, to name a few. Place each of these synonyms in the blank; When my man cheats he is _____ me.

_____

_____

_____

6. How does each sentence make you feel? Is there a synonym that equates to respect that you can associate with cheating? Is it true that there is no way for cheating and being respectful to exist in the same sentence? Going forward will you continue to repeat the above sentences and apply these truths to your way of thinking, or will you choose to consider his cheating respectful?

_____

_____

_____

7. How can a man take care of home and cheat at the same time? Isn't his cheating taking away from his attention to the home? Isn't he taking away time, energy, and money to cheat?

_____

_____

_____

8. Is the belief that cheating can be respectful shielding you from emotional distress? Does it cause you to feel less lonely to believe your man is being respectful as he cheats?

_____

_____

_____

9. Have you in fact created a way to reward your man for being slick and sneaky with his cheating? As long as he continues to cover his tracks, will you consider his cheating respectful?

_____

_____

_____

10. To assist with reconnecting with your core values, go back down memory lane. How did you feel the first time he cheated? List the emotions, feelings, and thoughts as you re-experience the memory of the first time he cheated. Did you consider it possible for him to respectfully cheat at that time? Has this belief grown out of your decision to stay with your cheater or from your core values?

_____

_____

11. Does the concept of respectful cheating make you feel less naïve, used, or foolish for staying?

_____

_____

_____

12. You re-wrote your rules and boundaries for your relationship after you stayed with him. What were the original rules and boundaries you set before you created the concept of respectful cheating? What were the original expectations before you began bargaining with yourself and compromising your standards?

_____

_____

_____

13. Are you enabling his cheating? By re-writing your rules and boundaries, have you given him a manuscript on how to be a respectful cheater instead of holding him to the original standard of respecting his commitment to you?

_____

_____

_____

14. Did you buy into the concept of respectful cheating in order to assist with respecting yourself for staying? Are you finding comfort in the misfortune of other women by comparing their ugly mess to your pretty mess? When you hear, read, or witness something you consider far worse than his cheating, does that give you validation to stay with your respectful cheater?

_____

_____

15. Are you getting a false sense of respect and pride from the misery of other women who have been cheated on in a more disrespectful manner? Are you getting a false sense of worth from pitying the circumstances of other women who aren't as lucky as you to be with a "respectful cheater?" Are you getting a false sense of boundaries from deceiving yourself into believing there is a respectful way for your man to cheat? Have you created a false sense of reality?

_____

_____

_____

16. When your man is cheating, is his commitment to you as strong as his commitment to his cheating?

_____

_____

_____

17. What woman who cares about herself would not care that her man is cheating? How does not caring that he cheats minimize your ability to attend to your own needs and wants?

_____

_____

_____

18. Can you take pride in vowing to stay with your cheating man because he is respectfully cheating? Can you honor the fact that you are staying with a man you know will continue to cheat?

_____

_____

_____

19. What you really mean to say is your man cheats in accordance with the new distorted boundaries you have set? Have you set the stage for him not to honor or respect you by accepting his respectful cheating? By compromising the true nature of cheating, are you setting yourself up to compromise your true need for fidelity and loyalty? How have you disregarded yourself to make his cheating respectful?

_____

_____

_____

Now, having answered all the questions, what is your truth?

REWRITE YOUR TRUTH

Congratulations! You are well on your way to honoring your truth. By answering the questions, you have begun the necessary work to increase your awareness of patterns and thoughts that have kept you stuck with a cheater. Challenge the lies you have told yourself, and rewrite your story below to reveal your ultimate truth. This is the beginning of getting unstuck.

_____

_____

_____

_____

_____

_____

_____

_____

_____

_____

_____

_____

_____

_____

_____

_____

Made in United States
North Haven, CT
30 March 2022